HOW TO TACKLE PUZZLES, UNRAVEL RIDDLES, CRACK CODES, AND OTHER WAYS TO BEND YOUR BRAIN

by Andrea Menotti

SCHOLASTIC INC.

New York Toronto London Auckland Sydney

Mexico City New Delhi Hong Kong Buenos Aires

ISBN: 0-439-57905-8

Design: Julie Mullarkey Gnoy
Illustrations: Kelly Kennedy

12 11 10 9 8 7 6 5 4 3 2 1 4 5 6 7 8 9/0

Printed in the U.S.A.

First Scholastic printing, June 2004

CONTENTS

How to Survive This Book

So, where do you keep your **most important survival tool**? On the top shelf of your closet? Under your mattress? In your sock drawer? No way! Your most important survival gear can only be found in one very special place: **between your ears**!

That's right—the one gadget that you'll need to count on every time you wind up in a tough spot is **your very own trusty and talented brain**! That's why this month's *How to Survive Anything* book is dedicated to your mental muscles. Like all muscles, your brainy ones need a good workout to stay strong and get stronger—and **this book is packed with puzzles that'll get your cranium all revved up** and ready for whatever challenges life throws your way!

This book will give you:

- **strategies to tackle brainteasers**.
- **different types of brainteasers** so you can flex your different mental muscles.
- **lots of opportunities to make your own brainteasers**, because you're *really* a mental master when you can tease *other* people's brains!

River Crossing!

This month's book comes with a great brain-boggling game called **River Crossing**. It takes some skill and know-how to play, so turn to page 38 for hints on mastering this challenge!

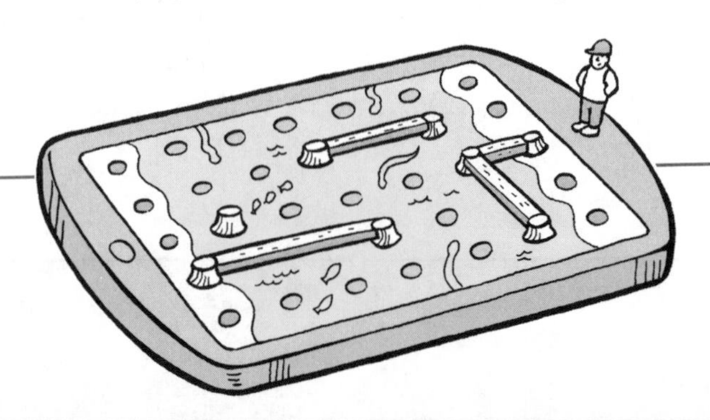

How to Get the Best Brain Workout

The **answers to all the puzzles in this book** are waiting for you on pages 72–80.

But don't peek! Because if you really want a **mental muscle workout**, you're going to have to get those answers the hard way: by pumping and churning and tugging and digging them out of your own brain! Sure, sometimes you might be stumped for a while, but **don't give up**! Looking at the answer before you've *really* wrestled with a brainteaser is like:

- a weightlifter putting down a barbell as soon as it feels heavy.

- a runner turning around whenever she reaches a hill.

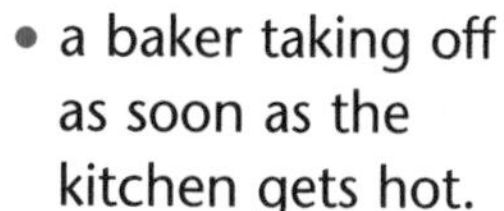

- a baker taking off as soon as the kitchen gets hot.

Some brainteasers can be really tough—but you can take the heat. Anytime a puzzle leaves you stumped, **give yourself a pep talk**. Say to yourself: *I can do it!* And then **give yourself some time**. No one's holding a stopwatch. **You can think about a puzzle as long as you want, whenever you want**—while you shower, ride the school bus, walk the dog, empty the dishwasher, or whatever. Hopefully, you'll have a wonderful **a-ha moment** when you finally discover the answer (and won't that feel great!).

And if you *don't* have an a-ha moment, that's okay. You tried, and that's what matters. You'll be more equipped to take on the *next* tricky one, because **the more you wrestle with tough puzzles, the tougher *you'll* get**!

WHAT KIND OF PUZZLE BUSTER ARE YOU?

With this quiz, you'll get a taste of the **different kinds of puzzles** you'll find in this book, so you can decide where you want to start your workout.

1. **Which one of these words doesn't belong?**

   keep, live, loose, spool, peek, evil, loops

2. **Can you figure out these two words? They're spelled exactly the same except for *one* letter, but they mean very different things.** Clues are below the blanks.

   ________________ - K + H = ________________

   People do this when they like each other a lot — Cats make this sound when they don't like something

3. **What common phrase does this box bring to mind?**

   Dog ←
   Dog
   Dog

4. **What kind of bird is pictured here?**

5. **Can you draw this shape without picking up your pencil or retracing any lines?**

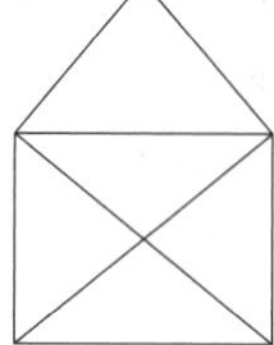

6. **What number belongs in place of the question mark?**

1	3	4	5	2
4	6	2	2	3
5	9	6	7	?

7. Looking at the first two scales, how many triangles will balance the final scale?

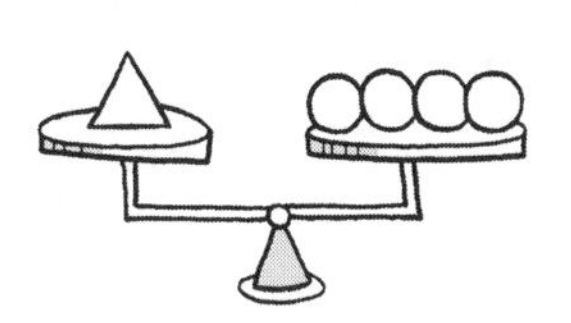

8. Here's part of a coded message. Which symbol do you think might stand for the letter I?

9. In the coded message above, which symbol do you think might represent the letter E?

10. Which word becomes shorter when you add two letters?

How'd You Do?

You'll find the answers to the quiz questions on page 72. Check off each one you got right and give yourself a score from 1 to 10. If you don't like your score, don't worry! **This book will show you how to master puzzles like these and many more.** Once you've learned some new strategies and tackled all the puzzles in the book, see if your score improves when you take the final pop quiz on page 69–71!

Oh, and if you're happy with your score—great! If there were particular questions you enjoyed most, check out the chart on the next page to see where you might want to go now.

What's Your Brain-Bending Style?

Read on to find out where you can find the different types of brainteasers in this book!

Questions 1–4:
If you liked these questions, turn to pages 9–35 for more **word whiz puzzles**!

Question 5:
You'll find more **visual puzzles** like this on pages 36–46.

Questions 6–7:
Look for more **number cruncher challenges** on pages 47–52.

Questions 8–9:
Check out pages 53–60 if you liked these **code cracking questions**.

Question 10:
If you like **riddles** or **trick questions** like this, turn to pages 61–69.

You might want to start with your favorite puzzles...or save the best for last! And if there's a kind of puzzle you don't like so much, or find really hard, give 'em a chance, too. You might like them better once you've mastered a couple of them later in this book!

How to Be a Word Whiz

How much do you know about words? Here's your chance to find out! You'll rhyme them, rearrange them, reverse them, build them, take them apart, and even transform them into their opposites. But before you dive in, read the tips below to get the scoop on word puzzles!

THE WORD WHIZ'S BAG OF TRICKS

Word puzzles often involve hunting for a word. Usually you'll get a clue to point you in the right direction, and then you'll have to find just the right word to solve the puzzle. How do you do that?

- **Become a wordhound.** You've heard of bloodhounds, right? They're good at tracking down missing people. *Wordhounds* search for—you guessed it—words. To be good at word puzzles, you'll need to make thorough searches of your vocabulary. For example, here's a little puzzle (like the ones on pages 11–13) where you need to find a pair of rhyming words that mean: **messy dad.**

So, think of as many words as you can that mean **messy**—like **untidy**, **cluttered**, **dirty**, and **sloppy**. Then think of other words for **dad**, like **father**, **pa**, **papa**, and **pop**.

Look at your collection of words—see if there's any way you can bend, twist, or squeeze them to make a rhyming pair...and with a little spark of imagination, you'll arrive at: **sloppy poppy**.

- **Try working backwards.** A lot of these word puzzles involve pairs of words. If the first word of the pair has you stumped, work on the second.

- **Cross-examine the clues.** Sometimes a word has more than one meaning. Make sure you've covered all the possible definitions.

- **Hit the books.** If you're really at your wit's end, then try using some of the sources below to help you. They can help jump-start your brain when you're stuck!

- **Thesaurus.** This handy resource will give you lists of synonyms (words with similar meanings) for the clues you're given in a puzzle.

- **Rhyming dictionary.** A rhyming dictionary is a great tool for when you're trying to solve rhyming pair puzzles (like on pages 11–13). If you think you've figured out one word in a pair, the rhyming dictionary will give you a list of words that rhyme with it.

- **Dictionary of common phrases.** At the end of this section, you'll have to hunt for *more* than just individual words—you'll need to come up with **whole phrases** or **idioms** (an "idiom" is a well-known saying or expression, like "head over heels in love"). If you have a hunch that the phrase you're looking for is about **hats**, check the index of your dictionary for all the phrases about hats. And hopefully you'll be able to **pull the rabbit out of the hat**!

So, **word whiz**, are you ready to get started?

RHYME TIME!

Each pair of words describes another pair of words that rhymes. Check out the example below:

EXAMPLE:

sad footwear = **blue shoe**

Got it? Good! Now, see if you can figure out these rhyming pairs!

1. bulky kitty

2. silly rabbit

3. insect embrace

4. kind rodents

5. unreal serpent

6. distant sun

7. female friend

8. cranium ache

9. no-cost plant

10. wet winner (damp ______)

11. fake horse (phony ______)

12. moist pooch (______ doggy)

13. large swine

14. stinky stomach

Rhyme Time II: Tough Stuff!

Think you've got the hang of it now? Great! Now try these new-o duos. They're a little tougher, but you've got the skill—and now you know the drill!

1. stationary quacker

2. energetic ape (spunky ______)

3. geeky parakeet

4. self-righteous insect (smug ______)

5. grumpy cat (______ tabby)

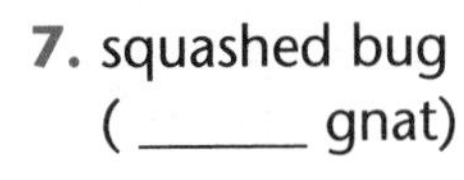

6. one-of-a-kind horse (______ mare)

7. squashed bug (______ gnat)

8. happy diploma-holder (______ grad)

You Can Make Your Own Rhyming Pairs!

Grab your rhyming dictionary (or find one online) and start working on your own pair puzzles. Begin with a noun (a person, place, or thing) and then come up with a rhyming word to describe it. Use a thesaurus to help you find your clues, then challenge your friends to figure out your rhyming pairs!

ANAGRAM PAIRS

An **anagram** is a word that's made from the same letters as another word. Here's an example (notice how the words have the same letters):

listen = silent

A special kind of anagram is a **reverse anagram** where a new word is made by spelling a word backwards, like:

spool

loops

In this puzzle challenge, you'll need to find a pair of anagrams to fit the clues given in each set. One of the pairs is a reverse anagram. Can you spot it?

EXAMPLE:

finest wagers = **best bets**

1. naked grizzly

2. famous rodents

3. inexpensive fuzzy fruit

4. feline performance

5. pale brown-colored picnic pest

The ones on this page are a little bit tougher, so some of them have upside-down hints at the bottom of the page—but only if you want them!

6. aching flower

7. big syrup-producing tree

8. snake gift

9. beast teachers

10. disliker of our planet

11. sea-faring boat

Hints: *7. (ample ______), 8. (serpent ______), 9. (______ mentors), 10. (______ hater)*

You Can Make Your Own Anagram Pairs!

If you want some help rearranging your words, hop on the Internet and find an anagram machine. Just type "anagram" into your favorite search engine. Then type your favorite words into the machine and see what comes up!

Plus T

In this challenge, you'll get clues for two words. **Add a T** anywhere in the first word to get the second word.

EXAMPLE:

tile plus T = title

clues: shower wall covering / the name of a book

1. ______ plus T = ______

clues: winter sport equipment (just one, not two) / a short play

2. ______ plus T = ______

clues: billy goats have these / a rose has these

3. ______ plus T = ______

clues: to stitch / a thick soup

4. ______ plus T = ______

clues: opposite of "walk" / the smallest one in a litter

5. ______ plus T = ______

clues: opposite of "lose" / a matched pair

6. ______ plus T = ______

clues: opposite of "young" / to have informed

7. ______ plus T = ______

clues: combat / a bump on a toad

8. ______ plus T = ______

clues: a feast / iron and steel are types of ______

9. ______ plus T = ______

clues: a sound used to scare someone / type of shoe worn by cowboys (one of the pair)

10. ______ plus T = ______

clues: an expression of pain / one of the five senses

11. ______ plus T = ______

clues: to listen / your blood pumper

12. ______ plus T = ______

clues: our star / to shock

You Can Make Your Own Plus Pairs!

You don't have to use T—use another letter and see what you can add up!

What about L?

BET + L = **BELT**

What about R?

HUT + R = **HURT**

CROSS YOUR T'S!

Here you'll find two words—the first one has an uncrossed t in it (otherwise known as a lowercase L). **Cross the t** to get the second word. Clues are below the blanks.

EXAMPLE:

meal cross T → meat

clues: lunch or dinner / beef or chicken

1. ______ cross T → ______

clues: a soccer player scores this / a sheep-like animal

2. ______ cross T → ______

clues: a cross between a donkey and a horse / can't speak

3. ______ cross T → ______

clues: to get better / warmth

4. ______ cross T → ______

clues: ring the ____ / something you wear that holds your pants up

5. ______ cross T → ______

clues: a mess / to end

6. ______ cross T → ______

clues: a gadget like a hammer or a saw / the sound a horn makes

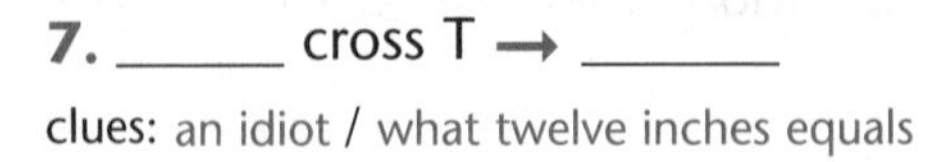

7. ______ cross T → ______

clues: an idiot / what twelve inches equals

8. ______ cross T → ______

clues: not fast / to store away

9. ______ cross T → ______

clues: a marine animal with flippers / a place to sit

Double Trouble!

In this challenge, you'll add a doubled letter (like bb, dd, ff, or gg) to the first word to get the second. After you finish, you'll be seeing double (just kidding!). Clues are below the blanks to help you out.

EXAMPLE:

hay plus double letter = happy

clues: a horse eats this / glad

1. ______ plus double letter = ______

clues: to purchase something / another word for "rabbit"

2. ______ plus double letter = ______

clues: opposite of tan (when you haven't been to the beach all summer) / equipment to play ping pong

3. ______ plus double letter = ______

clues: dime, nickel, or quarter / a box for someone who has died

4. ______ plus double letter = ______

clues: the opposite of "night" / another word for "father"

5. ______ plus double letter = ______

clues: the month after April / to wed

6. ______ plus double letter = ______

clues: the color you get when you mix white and black together / another word for "grandma"

7. ______ plus double letter = _________

clues: a horse-like animal / a harness for a dog's mouth

8. ______ plus double letter = ______

clues: a unit of distance (when you're traveling) / not the beginning or the end, but the ______

9. ______ plus double letter = ______

clues: if you don't buy something at full price, you get it on _____ / what you put on a horse before you ride it

10. ______ plus double letter = ______

clues: a river in Egypt / to take tiny bites

11. ______ plus double letter = ______

clues: a tool for shaping fingernails / another word for "violin"

You Can Make Your Own Double Trouble!

Think of words that have double letters, and then see what would happen if you took the double letters away. You might find it helpful to use your rhyming dictionary again, because you can find more words with double letters that way. Make up clues, and then see if your friends can figure 'em out!

MORE DOUBLE TROUBLE!

In this challenge, you'll double one of the letters in the first word to make the second word. Read the clues below each pair, and then fill in the blanks!

EXAMPLE:

hop double one of the letters = hoop

clues: a small jump / you shoot a basketball through this

1. ______ double one of the letters = ______

clues: to gamble / a dark red root vegetable

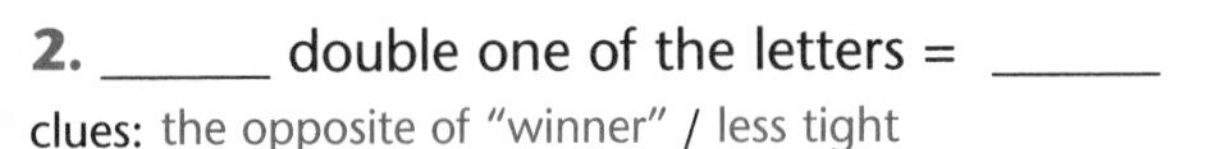

2. ______ double one of the letters = ______

clues: the opposite of "winner" / less tight

3. ______ double one of the letters = ______

clues: one who wounds with teeth / something that has a harsh taste, like horseradish

4. ______ double one of the letters = ______

clues: to let go of something accidentally / to sag

5. ______ double one of the letters = ______

clues: the color of blood / a thin, hollow piece of wood

6. ______ double one of the letters = ______

clues: you use this to smell with / a loop of rope tied with a knot is called a ______

7. ______ double one of the letters = ______

clues: the opposite of "go" / to bend down

8. ______ double one of the letters = ______

clues: to go bad / the part of a plant under the ground

Shhh! Silent E Pairs

Adding a silent E really changes the sound of a word. If you add an E to "kit," you get "kite." Add an E to "ton," you get "tone." How many silent E pairs can you think of? Try these...and then try to make some up for yourself!

1. ______ + e = ______

clues: something you wear on your head / the opposite of "love"

2. ______ + e = ______

clues: to slice / another word for "adorable"

3. ______ + e = ______

clues: the opposite of "off" / _____, two, three, four...

4. ______ + e = ______

clues: the opposite of "from" / a part of your foot

5. ______ + e = ______

clues: a floor covering (you wipe your feet on it before coming into your house) / a friend (a word used in Britain)

WORD MAGIC

Okay, word whiz, time to whip out your wand! You're going to turn COLD into WARM! HARD into SOFT! RAGE into CALM! By changing one letter at a time, you'll take one word and turn it into another very different word. The trick is that each step has to be a real word. Check the example below for inspiration, and then work your own magic on the next two pages.

EXAMPLE:

Turn TREE into SEED

Remember, only one letter can change per step. In this example, the underlined letter is the one that has changed in each step.

TREE

FREE

FRET

FEET

FEED

SEED

Now test your word powers on the nine transformations below! Fill in the blanks—changing one letter from the word above it—and see the words morph before your very eyes! (We've filled in some of the words to help you out, but you can ignore them if you'd like and get there on your own.)

1. RAGE to **CALM** *(4 steps)*

RAGE

______

PALE

______

CALM

2. COLD to **WARM** *(4 steps)*

COLD

______

CARD

______

WARM

3. HAND to **FOOT** *(5 steps)*

HAND

______

BOND

______

______

FOOT

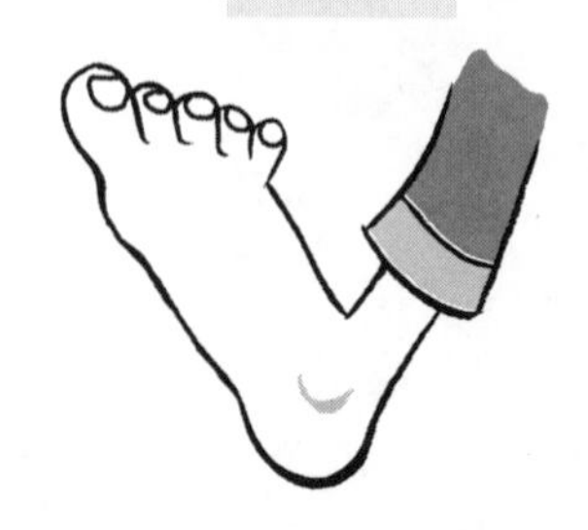

4. TALL to **WIDE** *(5 steps)*

TALL

______

______

MADE

______

WIDE

5. HARD to **SOFT** *(6 steps)*

HARD

______

______

CORE

______

______

SOFT

6. ROCK to **GOLD** *(7 steps)*

ROCK

______

SICK

______

______

MILD

______

GOLD

7. DEAD to **LIVE** *(8 steps)*

DEAD

______

______

SELL

______

______

FILE

______

LIVE

Survival Tip

If you get stuck working your way down from the top word, try working your way up from the bottom word instead.

8. SEED to **ROSE** *(9 steps)*

SEED

______

______

FEAT

______

______

PEST

______

______

ROSE

9. MINI to **HUGE** *(12 steps)*

MINI

______

______

LEND

______

______

HARD

______

______

HATS

______

______

HUGE

You Can Make Your Own Word Magic!

Choose two four-letter words (it's best if the words are somehow related—like opposites) and see if you can transform one into the other. Or, just start with a favorite word and keep transforming it till you get a word you like. Then give your friends your pair and see if they can work the same magic!

Word Pyramids

Now let's go to ancient Egypt, the land of the pyramids! Each pyramid starts with a two-letter word at the top. Add one letter anywhere in the next row to make a new word. The clue next to each row will tell you the word that belongs there.

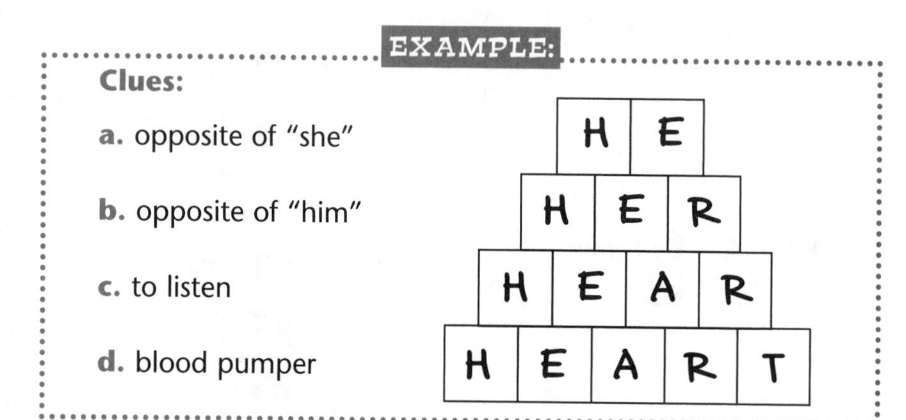

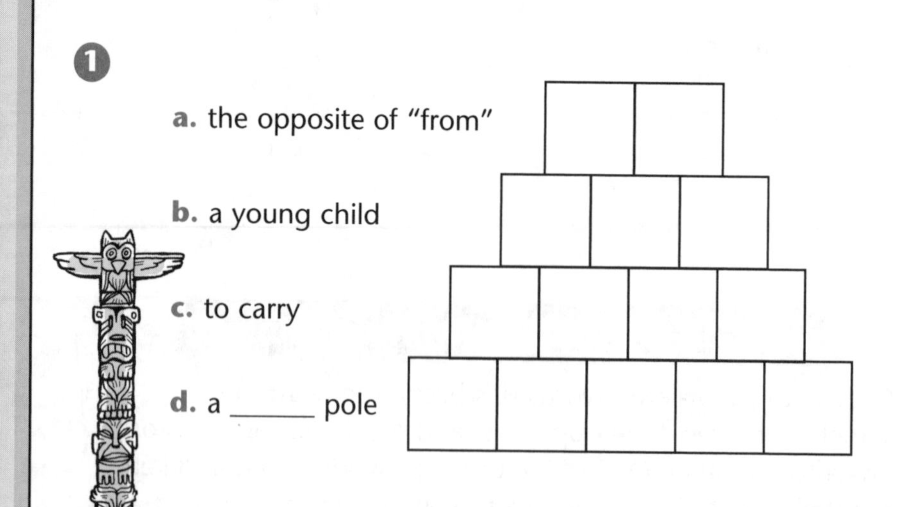

2

a. the opposite of "stop"

b. the past tense of "get"

c. a barnyard animal

d. to show off

3

a. ______ what?

b. another word for "soil"

c. the opposite of "bought"

d. not liquid like water, but ______ like an ice cube

4

a. don't worry, ______ happy!

b. wanna ______?

c. the opposite of "worst"

d. another word for "monster"

5

a. another word for "dad"

b. a frying ______

c. what you feel when you've hurt yourself

d. the opposite of "fancy"

6

a. if a pencil belongs to you, you say, "that's ______ pencil"

b. mother, ______ I?

c. lots of something

d. another word for "bully"

7

a. not you, but ______

b. the past tense of "meet"

c. ______ morphosis (or what a caterpillar goes through to become a butterfly)

d. gold, lead, and aluminum are types of ______

You Can Make Your Own Pyramids!

Here's a pyramid for you to finish. Figure out a word to fit in each row, and then create the clues. Check out page 74 to see what we came up with, and then see if a friend can fill in your pyramid!

Clues:

a. a book, ___ apple, an egg

b.

c.

d.

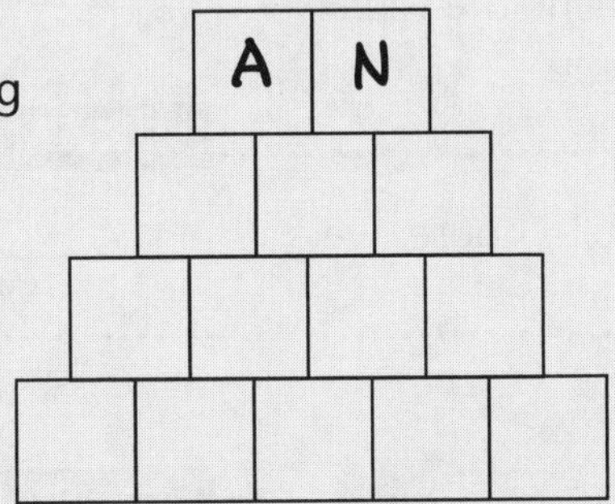

CHOCO-CHALLENGE

You can make lots of great things with chocolate, like cookies, cake, and candy... but how many words can you make out of the letters **C-H-O-C-O-L-A-T-E**? Here are some examples: **coat**, **hotel**, **to**, **eat**, and **late**. Write all the words you can find on a separate sheet of paper, and look below to see how you score!

Score yourself!

35 words or more: *Champion Chocoholic*

20 to 34 words: *Hot Cocoa Kid*

10 to 19 words: *Choc Jock*

9 words or less: *Try Vanilla!*

Check page 74 to see a bunch of words you can make from the word "chocolate"!

TRIPLETS

You had your fun with doubles on pages 19–22? Now it's time to try out some triples! The three words in each of the sets on these two pages have something in common: they'll each form a compound word (or a two-word phrase) when one word is added in front or behind it. Your challenge is to figure out which word will link the triplets.

EXAMPLE:

bulb, house, weight ______ light

(lightbulb, lighthouse, lightweight)

EXAMPLE:

over, rack, rain ______ coat

(overcoat, coat rack, raincoat)

1. easy, arm, wheel ______

2. mail, door, snow ______

3. tug, life, paddle ______

4. hot, bull, mad ______

5. bus, door, rest ______

6. butter, horse, dragon ______

7. flower, tea, hole ______________________________

8. dog, doll, tree ______________________________

9. car, amusement, national ______________________________

10. point, park, foot ______________________________

11. oak, family, apple ______________________________

12. up, joy, match ______________________________

13. cake, burger, blue ______________________________

14. time, sewing, gun ______________________________

15. brain, blue, cage ______________________________

16. time, oat, worm ______________________________

17. crust, mud, apple ______________________________

18. box, race, sick ______________________________

19. man, wrist, tower ______________________________

Find-a-Fruit!

Can you find seven fruits in this bowl? You can make words by going up, down, sideways, or diagonally, and you can use the letters more than once in a word. We've found "grape" to get you started.

Dress Up!

Can you find seven items of clothing in this dresser?

Desk Quest

Can you find the eight supplies in this desk?

You Can Make Your Own Word Hunt Box!

First, decide on a location—maybe a jewelry box, a gym locker, or a garage—then pick about six items (or more) that belong in your location. Make sure they're short words that have some letters in common. Draw a grid of squares (like the ones shown here) and put your most-used letters in the center of the box. Keep rearranging the letters in the grid until you get an arrangement that works!

A Picture's Worth ONE word!

Ever hear people say that a "picture's worth a thousand words"? Each of these pictures is a drawing of a word. Can you figure out which word? Try it, then check page 75 for the answers.

1.

2.

3.

4.

5.

You Can Make Your Own Picture Puzzles!

Can you make a picture of:

1. bulldoze
2. starstruck
3. crackpot

See page 75 in the Answer Key to see an example for each! Can you think of more words that can be turned into pictures? How many can you make?

Phrase in a Box!

These are diagrams of a word or phrase. Can you figure out what each means? (Here's a hint: don't overlook the placement of the words—it can mean a lot!)

1.

2.

3.

POPPD

4.

COLLAR
HOT

5.

6.

7.

8.

9.

10.

11.

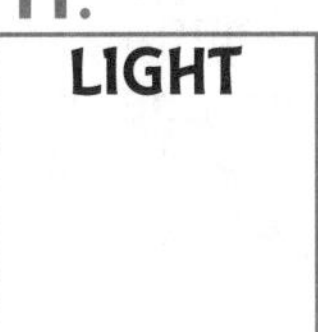

12.

13.

14.

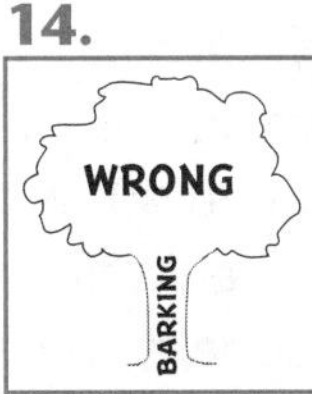

15.

16.

You Can Make Your Own Phrase Boxes!

Try making your own boxes for the following phrases: **cut corners, banana split, top secret**. Once you're done, see page 75 to see what we came up with!

How to Master Visual Puzzles

Now that you've had your fun with words, it's time to turn your attention to a whole different kind of puzzle, where shapes and lines (and planks and stumps!) take the place of words and letters. You'll draw pictures in a single pencil stroke, fold up imaginary cubes, create mirror images, forge paths across raging rivers, and more!

Picture It Now!

Here in the land of visual puzzles, your **mind's eye** is your best friend. That's the place in your brain where you can **picture** or **imagine** things. You use your mind's eye when you imagine a picture you're going to draw, a snow fort or sand castle you're going to build, or when you plan how you're going to rearrange the furniture in your room. You see things not only as they *are*, but as they will be *after* you've created or changed them.

To solve the puzzles in this section, you'll use your mind's eye to the max. For example, on page 40, when you're given a flat, unfolded cube, you can (in your mind's eye) fold it up with your imaginary hands and get a peek at how it will look.

Give Your Mind's Eye a Hand

Try these ideas:

Get a hold on the fold. Draw this unfolded cube onto your own sheet of paper. You can use the pictures shown here (or create your own)—but make sure each picture you draw has a clear right-side-up and upside-down direction. Then cut out your drawing and fold it (and tape it—there are tabs on the drawing to make this easier) into a cube. Notice which sides are next to each other and how the picture on each side looks. Unfold and refold and get to know the cube as well as you can. This will help your mind's eye do its job later.

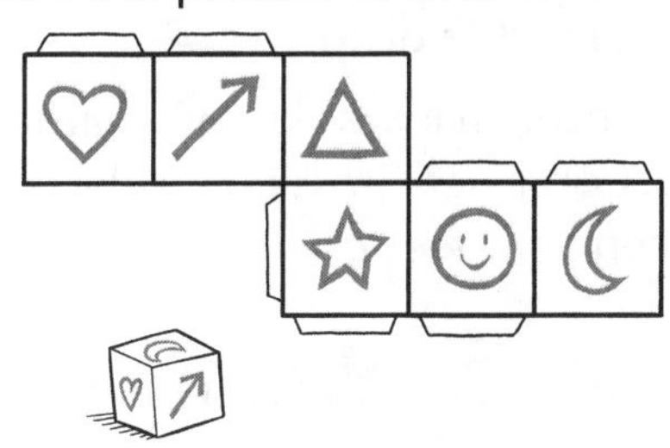

Take some time to reflect. To help your mind's eye imagine mirror images, you can—drum roll, please!—hold things up to a mirror! Notice especially how things like letters, numbers, and clocks look when they're reflected (they're backwards, right?).

To get more practice with reflections, try this: on a blank sheet of paper, draw a line down the middle. This is your "mirror line." Draw a crazy shape or write a word on one side of the line. Hold it up to a mirror, and then sketch its reflection on the other side. As you draw, remember that a line or letter that slants toward your mirror line on one side should slant toward the mirror line on the other side, too. To check your work, just hold it up to a mirror again!

Try and try and try again. For cutting and drawing puzzles (like on pages 44 and 45), there's just no substitute for good old trial and error. That means you get out your pencil and plenty of scrap paper, and you try the puzzle many different ways until you find the solution. For coin and toothpick puzzles like the ones on page 46, using real coins and real toothpicks will help you work out possible solutions.

Trial and error is also a good approach to puzzles like **River Crossing,** the game you got this month. While you're trying to find your way across the river, you can move your planks around a much as you want, so you can test out various strategies. You can always return the planks to their original positions and start again i you reach a dead end.

So, now that you know what to expect, read on to get your feet wet on River Crossing...although in this game, you'll hopefully keep your feet *dry*!

How to Win at River Crossing

River Crossing is a real visual puzzler's kind of game. To win at it, you need to use your mind's eye to visualize your path across the raging rapids.

To start, read the directions booklet that came with it. Here's a quick review of the basic moves:

1. The hiker can only walk on planks to get from stump to stump.

2. The hiker can pick up and move any plank he has reached.

3. The hiker can only carry one plank at a time as he walks, and he can use the plank to walk on, if needed.

4. The hiker can set the plank down to create a path to another stump, as long as the plank fits perfectly between the stumps.

As you start each River Crossing challenge, ask yourself these questions:

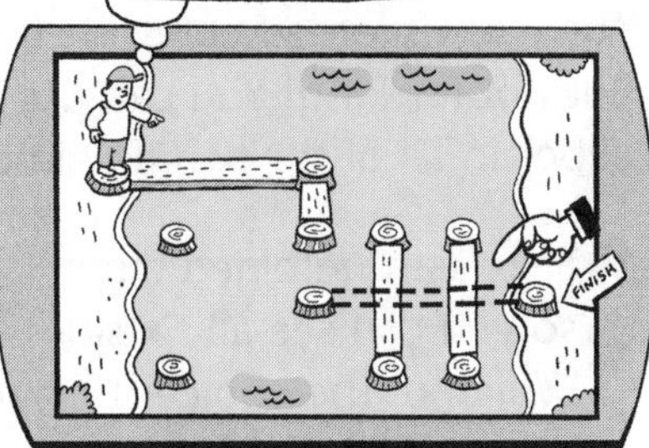

- **Where are you headed?** Where will you have to place your final plank to get to shore? Which size plank will it be?

- **What's in the way?** Are there planks that block your path to the shore? If so, you need to figure out how to get them out of the way.

- **Where can each plank go?** Look at the position of each stump, and see which ones are far enough apart for each plank size you have available. Consider each of these possible positions as you plan your path across the river.

So, are you ready to brave the river now? Set up your first challenge and test the waters!

Survival Tip

River Crossing takes some getting used to, so don't worry! If you're really puzzled, just walk yourself through the solution to one of the puzzles, moving the planks as described in the instructions. The solutions are in a code language that can seem tricky at first, but if you stick with it and move the planks according to the instructions, you'll start to see how a successful river crossing works. Then you can try other crossings yourself!

NICE CUBES

The two unfolded cubes below look as flat as flat can be, right? But not for long! You can use your mind's eye to envision the cubes in all of their three-dimensional glory!

1. Here's an unfolded cube, so you can see all six sides. Which of the choices below is the *correct* folded version of the cube?

A.

B.

C.

D.

E.

2. Here's another unfolded cube. Which one is the *incorrectly* folded version?

A.

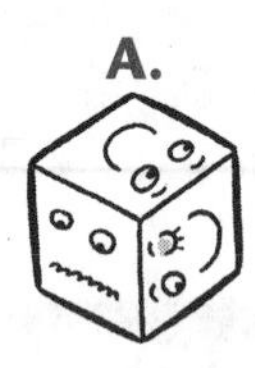

B.

C.

D.

E.

3. These three cubes are identical. Can you tell what's on the bottom side of each one just by looking at the other two cubes?

A.

B.

C.

Nice Dice

Dice are cubes, too. See if you can roll right through these two puzzles!

1. Can you tell which numbers are on the bottom of these two dice? (You have to know a little secret about the way dice are set up to do this puzzle. The secret is revealed on page 75.)

A. **B.**

2. Which one of these dice isn't set up in the usual way?

A. **B.** **C.** **D.**

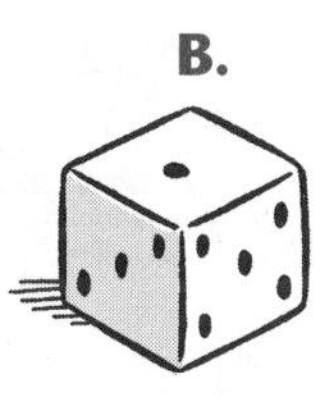

MIRROR MIRROR

If broken mirrors are bad luck, then these two pages are the most unlucky ones in the whole book! There are lots of wrong reflections here. Can you figure out which reflections are the right ones? (Remember: in a mirror, everything appears *backwards*.) Check page 76 to see if you're right!

1. Which of these pictures is the correct mirror image of this visual puzzler?

A.

B.

C.

D.

2. Which is the correct mirror image of this crazy shape?

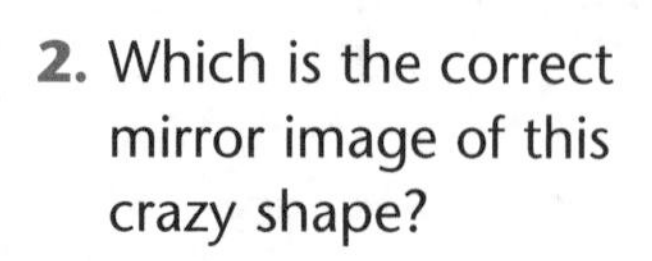

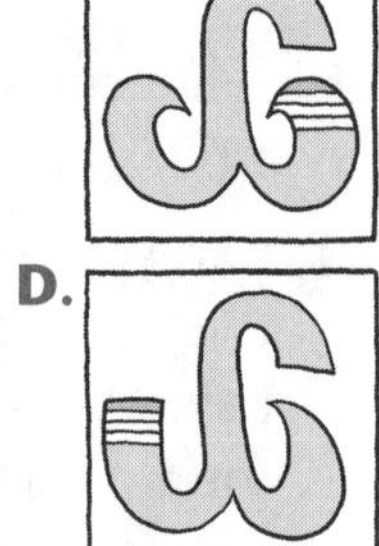

3. What about this work of modern art? Which version is the correct reflection?

4. Which reflected clock says 8:25?

Bonus Question: Which of these is the correct mirror image of the word "restaurant"?

restaurant

Flip Out!

Flip Out!

Now turn your mind's eye mirror upside down!

1. Which of these animal names will look exactly the same when turned upside down and reflected? To check, try turning this page upside down and drawing reflections of each of the words (using the technique on page 37).

CHICK EEL OX DOG HORSE

2. Which of these words will look exactly the same when flipped upside down and reflected?

ECHO CHEEK ICE CHOICE DECIDE CODE

Now Be a Mirror Yourself!

This lady can't find her mirror, and she wants to know how she looks in her new hat. Can you sketch a mirror image of her? Don't worry, it doesn't have to look exactly like her—she can't find her glasses, either! Just make sure to get the reflection right.

CUT IT OUT!

Now that you're done reflecting on mirrors, it's time to sharpen your knife. Okay, not a *real* knife—your imaginary one! Can you divide up these shapes?

1. Each of the kids at Chris's birthday party wants a piece of cake with a flower on it. There are seven kids (including Chris) and exactly seven flowers on the cake. Can you cut up the cake with only three straight cuts so everyone gets a flower? It's okay if the cake slices are different sizes—the kids only care about the flowers!

2. Farmer Ed has some very bad sheep. They won't stop squabbling, so he's decided to put them in their own separate enclosures. Can you help Farmer Ed build separate areas for each of his eleven sheep (keeping them exactly where they're standing now), with only four straight fences?

The Drawing Room

See if you can draw these five designs without lifting up your pencil or retracing any lines (it's okay to cross lines). But wait! There's a catch—one of these shapes can't be drawn without lifting up your pencil! Can you figure out which one is the dud?

1.

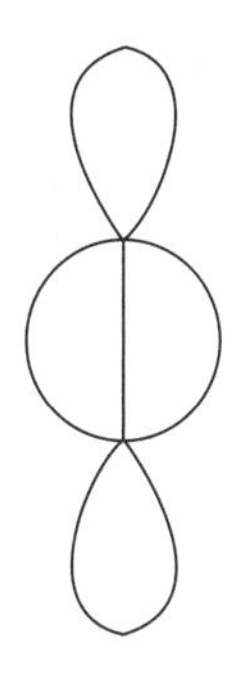

2.

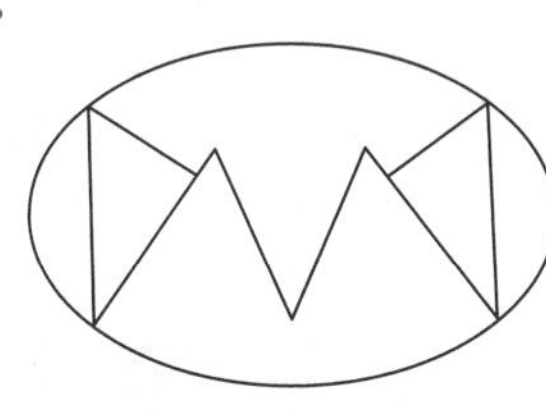

3.

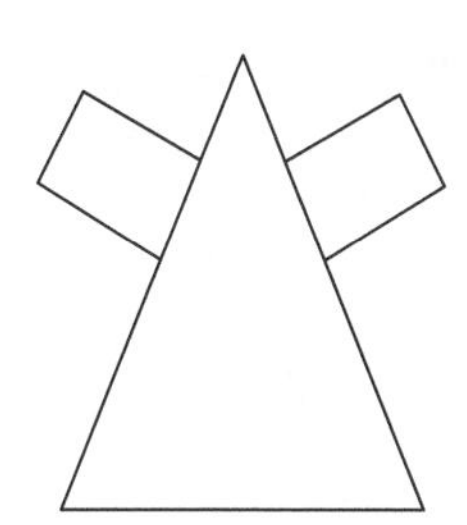

4.

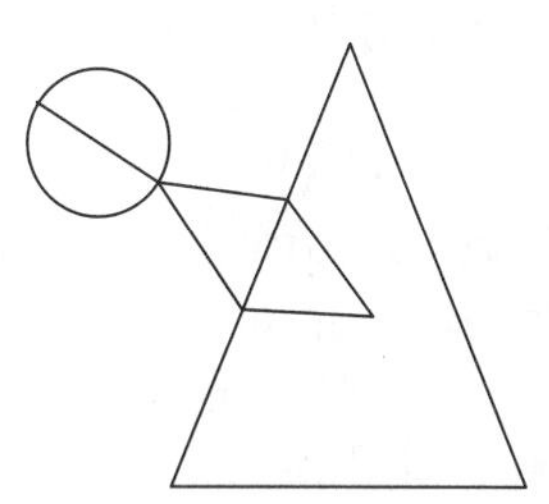

5.

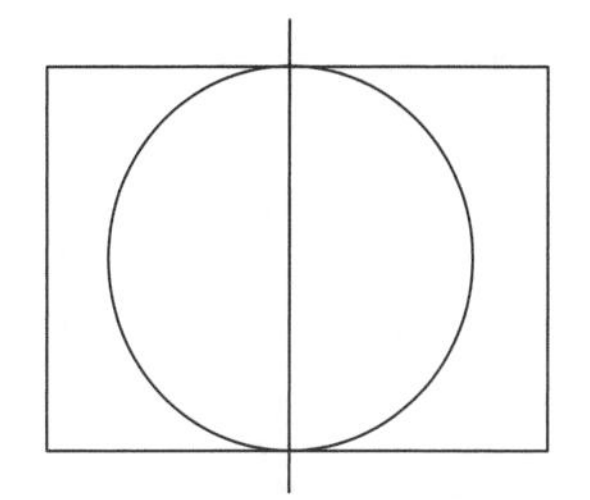

Pssst...

What's the secret to these shapes? How can you always know where to start and finish your single pencil line? Check the answers on page 76 for an explanation!

You Can Create Your Own One-Pencil-Line Designs

Once you've learned the secret to these puzzles, create your own shape—and challenge someone to draw it in one line!

Shifty Shapes

Think you're in pretty good shape now? Then grab a pile of pennies and a handful of toothpicks and try these challenges!

1. Flip this triangle upside down by moving only **three** coins.

2. Here are three triangles made out of toothpicks. Move **three** of these toothpicks to create five triangles.

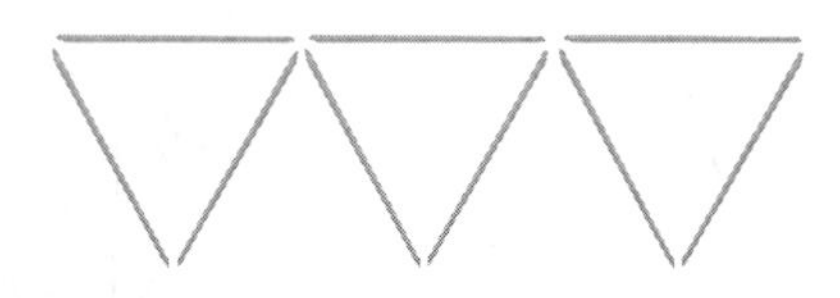

Bonus Questions!

1. This toothpick crab is facing the wrong way if it wants to eat its lunch. Can you turn it to face the snail by moving **three** of the toothpicks?

2. Albert is a little strange. Instead of saying "yes," he says "ya." He also changes his mind quite quickly. Can you make Albert say "no" by moving **two** toothpicks?

Shape Up!

Now try making your own coin or toothpick puzzles. Start with one shape, then see if you can switch to a very different shape in just a few moves. Challenge a friend to do the shape-change in as few (or fewer!) moves!

How to Be a Number Cruncher

Welcome to **number territory**, puzzler. Say hello to the natives—they've all come out to give you the official Numberland greeting, the high five!

You probably feel like you've known these numbers for (almost) your whole life—but wait till you see the fancy tricks they'll be pulling off in this next section!

To master these *numbersome* brain-benders, you'll need to:

- **Know how to add, subtract, multiply, and divide.** If you know how to do these four types of math, you've got it covered!
- **Try everything!** With puzzles like the ones on pages 48–49, you'll need to **try lots of different approaches**—adding, subtracting, multiplying, and dividing—until you discover the relationships between the numbers.
- **Don't give up!** Like the puzzles you tackled in the previous section, **trial and error** is the way to go. Just grab a pencil with a good eraser, pile up some scrap paper, and get going!

WHAT'S NEXT?

In each of the puzzles below, the numbers are arranged according to a secret system. Can you figure each one out and put the correct number in place of the question mark?

1.

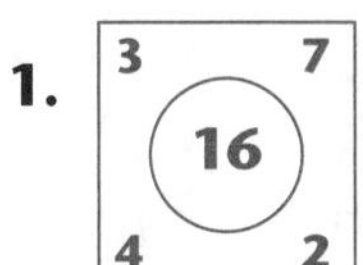

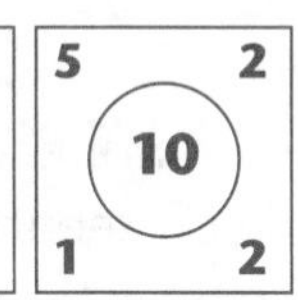

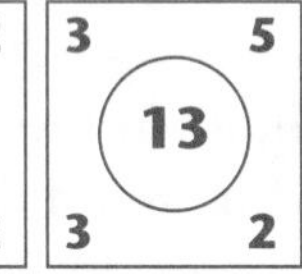

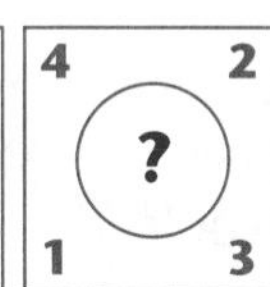

2.

5 2
3

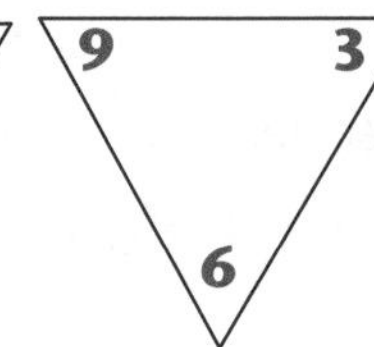

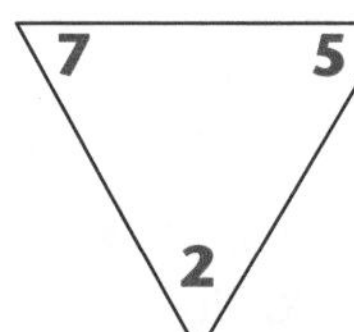

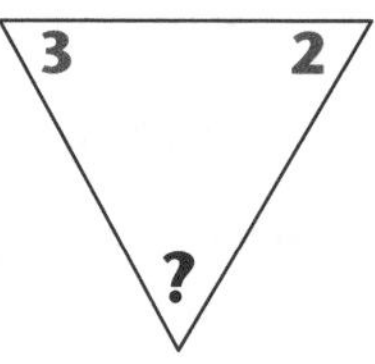

3.

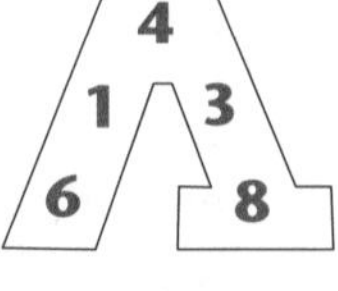

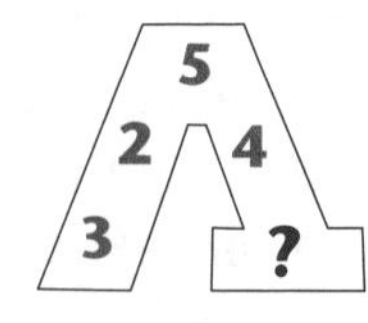

4.

2	2	3
1	9	

3	8	12
2	6	

4	5	7
3	8	

7	2	?
6	3	

5.

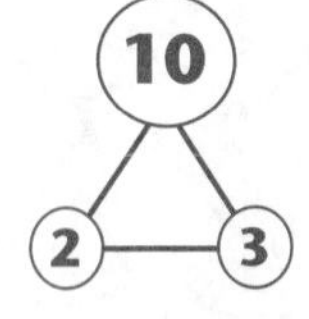

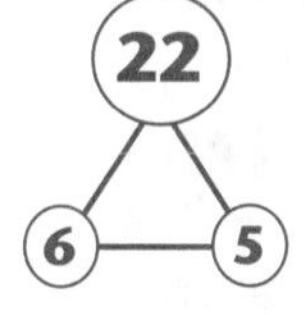

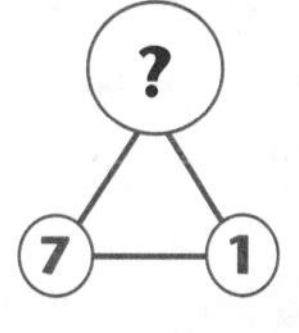

?
7 1

You Can Make Your Own Secret System!

Try making your own secret number system and see if a friend can catch on! Provide at least three examples to give your friend a chance to see a pattern.

Now What's Next?

If you got the secret number systems on the previous page, try these! In each case, you'll need to figure out which number goes in place of the question mark.

1.

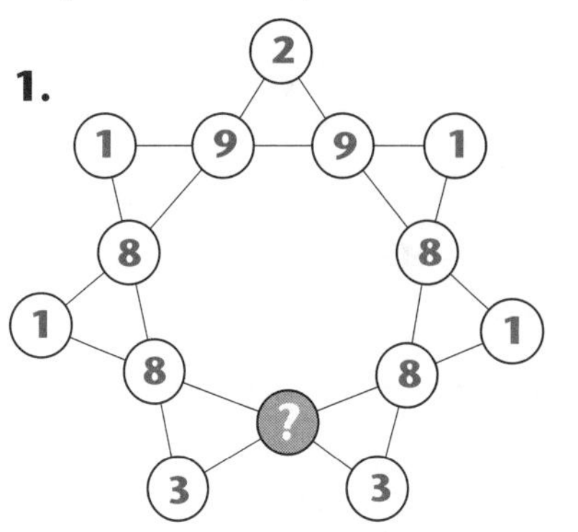

2.

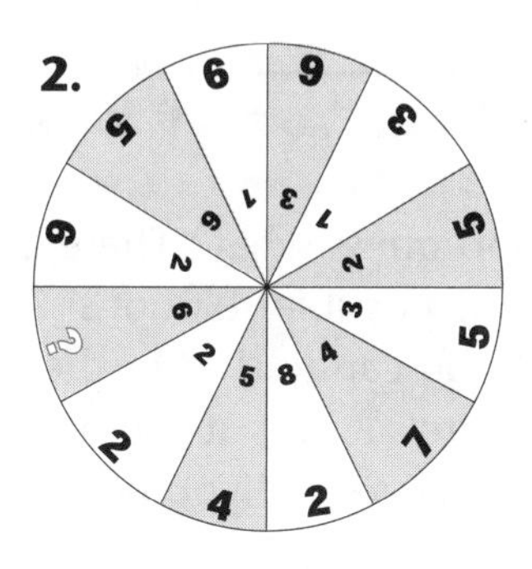

3.

9	1	8	2	7	3
6	4	5	5	4	6
3	7	2	8	1	?

4. This is a famous triangle called Pascal's Triangle, after a French mathematician and physicist named Blaise Pascal (1623–1662). Can you figure out which number belongs in place of the question mark?

Pascal was quite a calculating guy. When he was eighteen, he built a mechanical calculator that could add and subtract.

Bonus Question!

Can you figure out the six numbers that belong in the *next* row of Pascal's Triangle?

MATHEMAGIC

Ready for a little numerical **abracad-add-up**? Then see if you can work your magic on these math marvels.

1. **Arrange the numbers 1 through 6 in this magic triangle so that all sides have the same sum.** Oh, and guess what? There are four possible solutions! See if you can find all of them. There's a hint at the bottom of the page if you need it!

2. **Arrange the numbers 1 through 9 in this magic triangle so that the sum of each side equals 17.** There's a hint at the bottom of the page if you need it!

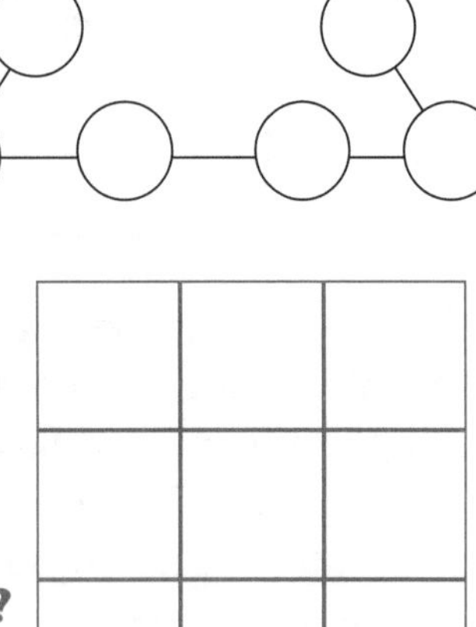

3. Here's a magic square that was invented thousands of years ago in ancient China. It's called the Lo Shu square. **Can you arrange the numbers 1 through 9 inside the boxes, so that all the rows and the diagonals add up to 15?** And yes, there's a hint at the bottom of the page, if you want it!

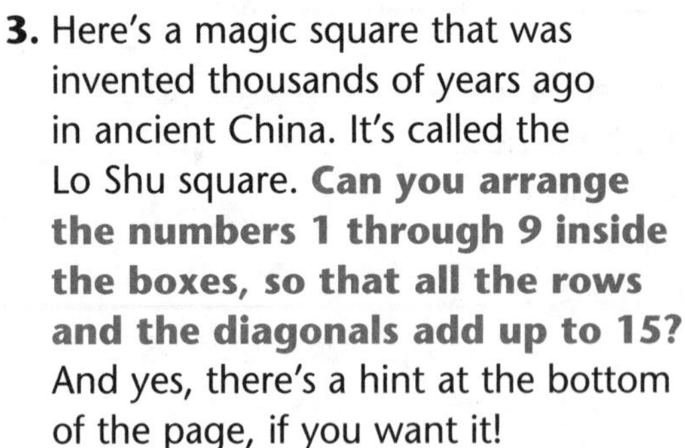

According to Chinese legend, the Lo Shu square was first discovered as a pattern on the shell of a giant tortoise that emerged from the River Lo ("shu" means turtle). It was believed that the square was magical, representing the natural order of the universe. Fifteen days, for example, is the number of days it takes for a new moon to become full.

Hint for #1: The sides can add up to 9, 10, 11, or 12.
Hint for #2: Put 1, 2, and 3 in the corners.
Hint for #3: Put 5 in the center.

Measure Up!

Ever had one of those days when you can't find all of your **measuring cups** or **egg timers**? Happens all the time, right? But once you finish with these number cruncher puzzles, that won't be a problem—you'll be a measurement master!

1. **Your chicken and stars soup needs 2 cups of water, but you only have 3-cup and 8-cup measures.** How will you measure exactly 2 cups?

2. **You need exactly 3 cups of sugar for your delicious specialty: chocolate fudge cake.** Unfortunately, all your measuring cups are missing except for your 5-cup and 12-cup measures. How will you measure exactly 3 cups?

3. **You need to boil your corn on the cob for 7 minutes.** Unfortunately, the technology in your kitchen is a little behind the times. You have only two hourglass-style egg timers: a 5-minute one and a 6-minute one. How will you get your *perfect* corn?

WEIGHT A MINUTE!

A **balance** allows you to check whether or not two weights are equal. For example, here's a pretty uneven balance:

Can you balance the final scale in each puzzle by looking at the other balanced scales?

1. The first three scales are balanced. How many **cookies** will balance the final scale?

= COOKIE

= CUPCAKE

= BREAD

= PIE

2. The first two scales are balanced. How many **bananas** will balance the final one?

?

How to Be a Code Cracker

Are you ready to enter the ♥◘ʃ ☻◄╬↕◄♥ world of codes, ciphers, spies, and sleuths? For a hint, check out the clue the Code Cracker is examining. (If you decoded it, ∂↕◄∞♥ ⌂◘○! The answer's on page 78 if you want to check.)

Being a great code cracker is all about making **smart guesses** based on what you know about language. There are some **sly secrets** you can learn that will help you see right through even the strangest-looking codes.

For example, imagine you're a **mouse**, and you're scurrying across the kitchen to a fantastic hunk of Swiss cheese. When you arrive, you discover a **mysterious message**:

It's in some kind of strange **pie code**! Something tells you that the message is pretty important, so you decide to decode it before you chow down. Fortunately, with some help from your friend the Code Cracker, you can decode it in a flash.

The Code Cracker's Sly Secrets

- **Which symbol appears most often in the message?** Certain letters are used very often in the English language—like **E** for English! That's right, E is the most commonly used letter in English, followed by **T, A, O, N, I, R,** and **S**. Count up the appearances of each symbol in the message and see what you discover!

Symbol	Number of Appearances
	II
	II
	~~IIII~~ I
	I
	II
	I

Symbol	Number of Appearances
	III
	II
	I
	I
	I

- **Your most common symbol** has a good chance of being **E**. Try inserting E for the most common symbol and see what happens:

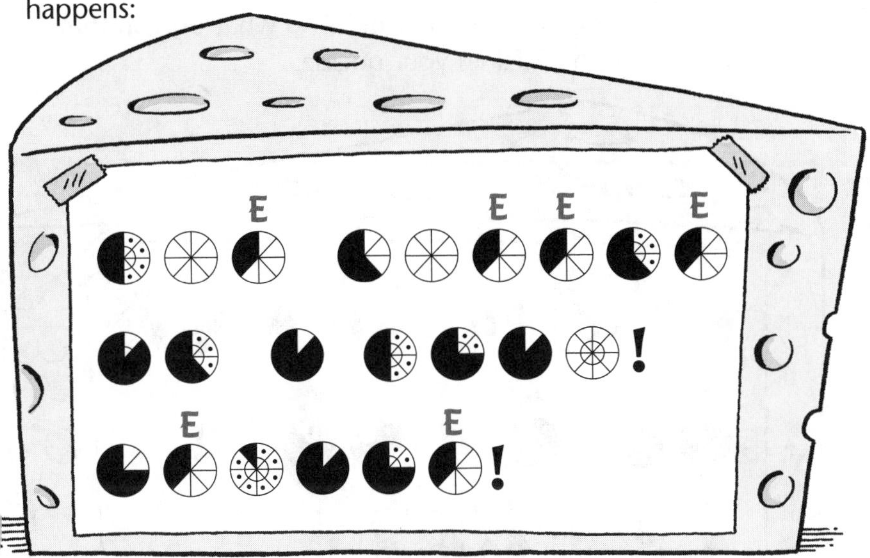

- **Do you have any clues to work with?** Do you know anything about what the message might be about or who it's for? Since this letter is attached to a piece of cheese, "cheese" would be a good guess for the second word:

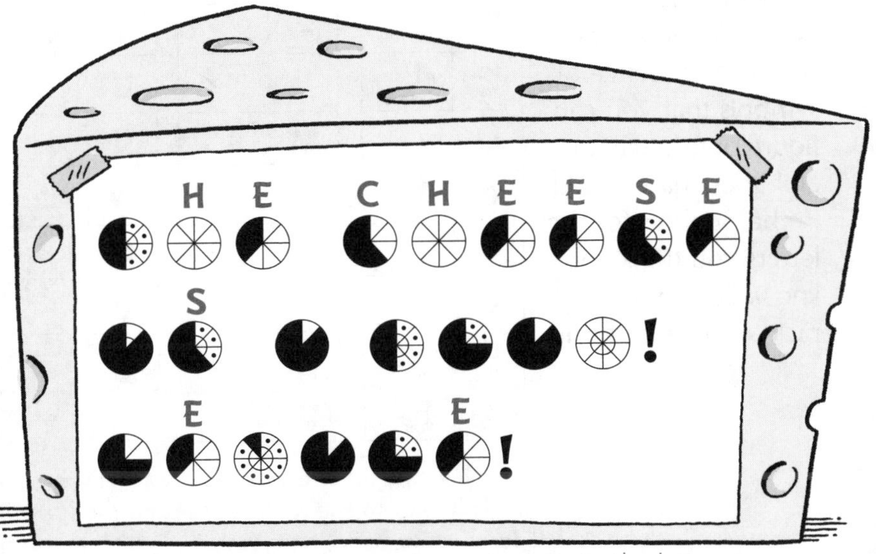

Since you think you know C, H, and S, you can write the letters in wherever those symbols appear anywhere else in the message.

- **Can you guess the easy little words?** How many two-letter words do you know that end with "S"? How many three-letter words do you know that end in "HE"? And what do you think that one-letter word is? Fill in your guesses.

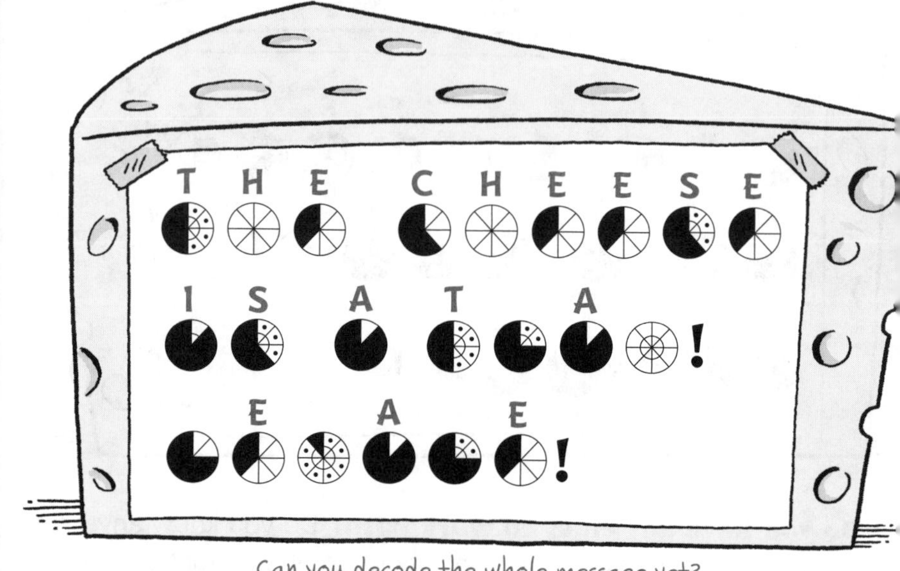

Can you decode the whole message yet?

- **Do you see any patterns in the code?** Some codes will be a sequence of symbols that you can figure out. Make an alphabet chart and fill in the symbols for the letters you think you know. See if you can pick up on a pattern.

A		J		S	
B		K		T	
C		L		U	
D		M		V	
E		N		W	
F		O		X	
G		P		Y	
H		Q		Z	
I		R			

Can you fill in the rest of the chart? You can find the key to the whole code (and the fully decoded message) on page 78.

What Big Eyes You Have

Think of the tragedy that could have been avoided if a certain little girl in a famous fairy tale had only learned the **eye code** before setting off to her grandmother's house....

Remember to look for the most common symbol (which is the letter E) and if you're stuck, there are some upside-down hints at the bottom of the page.

Hints: A= S=

ODE TO CODE

Can you decode this secret message? Hint: It's a **rhyming poem**. And luckily for you, the sender of this message didn't mind his **P's and Q's (or U's)**! See if the little scrap of information in the clue box can help you crack the code!

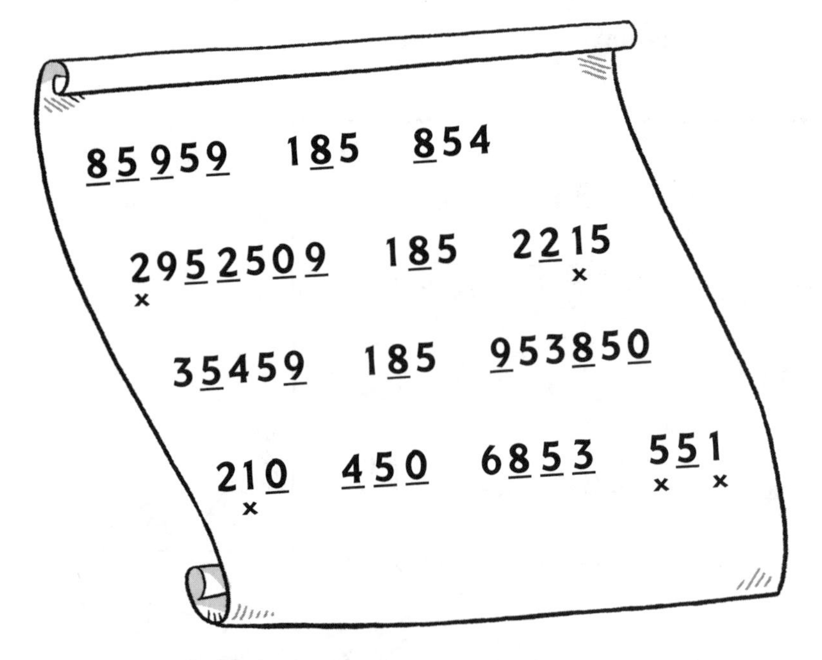

Need a Hint?

Stuck? You know that there are 26 letters in the alphabet, but only ten numbers (0–9). What are some other ways to make the symbols different? This code uses underlines and X'es under the numbers to make enough symbols for each letter.

Consider Yourself Warned

All three of the messages on pages 59–60 were sent by a helpful **Code Cracker** to warn these unsuspecting folks of dangers and surprises lurking nearby. The messages were all encoded with the same system. Can you figure it out using your code-cracking tricks? See if the picture clues help. There's an upside-down hint at the bottom of this page if you need help.

18-19-15-6 19-18,

8-22-19-6-19 23-7

15 16-19-19 3-2

13-3-9-6 22-19-15-18.

16-19-11-15-6-19.

18-19-15-6

4-6-19-7-8-3-2,

13-3-9'6-19 7-8-9-17-25

16-19-8-11-19-19-2

15 6-3-17-25 15-2-18

15 22-15-6-18

4-26-15-17-19.

Hint: All three messages begin with the word "dear".

18-19-15-6 24-19-15-2,

26-3-3-25-7 26-23-25-19

13-3-9-6 14-23-4-4-19-6

23-7 15-20-6-15-23-18

3-20 22-19-23-21-22-8-7.

How to Make *Your* Secret Messages Safer

If you'd like to send coded messages of your own, you can take the following steps to keep your secrets safer from prying eyes.

- **Remove the spaces between words.** That way, code crackers won't know where words begin and end, which will make it tougher for them to guess them.
- **Add symbols that don't mean anything.** Sprinkle them in throughout your messages. That'll really throw code crackers off!
- **Hide your message in plain sight.** If your message doesn't *look* like it's in code, code crackers won't even know it's there! Can you see the message hidden in the list on the right? If you use a code with letters, like the Caesar cipher, you can hide it like this. (Check page 79 to see if you've found the message!)

melon
eggs
ears of corn
tangerines
apples
turkey breast
tomato soup
watermelon
orange juice

How to Rule Riddles

Now that you've become a **practiced puzzle buster**, it's time to take on the sneakiest, slipperiest puzzles of them all: **riddles** and **trick questions**.

These puzzles will try to mislead you; they'll attempt to distract you and make you bark up the wrong tree, or they'll be vague and strange, seemingly impossible...but they're not! They're the kind of puzzle that'll make you say "of course!" when you realize the answer.

Trick or Trap

Here are some examples of sneaky questions. See if you can figure out the trick in each one!

1. If there are **seven apples** in a basket **and you take away five,** how many apples do you have?

2. A **raw egg** fell 15 feet without breaking. How did this happen?

3. After dinner, Marilyn said, "**I'm so sick of deserts**. I never want to see another one in my life." Yet she was very happy to eat an **ice cream sundae**. Why?

4. There's something a little **fishy** about the word **fortunate**. What is it?

5. When you take **two letters** away from a certain **five-letter word**, you're left with **one**. How is this possible?

6. Which is **heavier**, a pound of **feathers** or a pound of **bricks**?

7. Melanie had a box of **sixty-four crayons**. All but ten got lost somehow. How many did she have left?

8. Helen and Stella are next-door neighbors and like to run around the park, though they go in **opposite directions**. They run at exactly the same speed. However, it takes Helen **75 minutes** to circle the park, while it takes Stella **a whole hour and 15 minutes**. What's the difference?

9. A plane crashed just outside of **Dallas**, but no survivors were buried in **Texas**. Why not?

10. If Farmer Joe's **stallion** gives birth on Farmer Ed's property, who owns the pony?

How'd you do? Turn to page 79 to check your answers.

Sniff Out Trick Questions Where They Hide

Here are some basic tips you can use to catch the trick whenever a trick question tries to get *you*:

- **Read the question slowly**. A lot of trick questions (like #1, #6, #7, and #9 on pages 61–62) lose their "trick" when you slow them down. They're trying to pull a fast one, but if you carefully read each word, you'll see through the trickery!

- **Let no word or number go unstudied**. For questions like #3, #8, and #10, the key is to *really* know what important words or numbers mean.

- **Think of other meanings for important words**. In #4, you might have thought fishy meant "suspicious" at first, but here it just means "fish-like"!

- **Think about what's *not* said**. For questions like #2 and #5, think about the possibilities that the question leaves open. Did question #2 say that the egg fell *only* 15 feet? Question #5 wanted you to think you were left with "one *letter*," but did it say *one letter*, or just *one*?

So—think you're equipped to take on *more* riddles and trick questions? Then read on!

A-ha!

Get It?

Fooled Ya!

Spelling Spree

How's your spelling? Think it's pretty good? Then try these *tuff wons* and *sea* how *ewe dew*!

1. Can you spell a **five-letter word** that describes a **beach** using only **S** and **Y**?

2. If a funny gag is spelled **J-O-K-E**, and the stuff a fire produces is spelled **S-M-O-K-E**, then how do you spell **the white part of an egg**?

3. Is the state capital of California spelled **LOS ANGELES** or **LAS ANGELES**?

4. From which **seven-letter word** can you take away **two letters** and still be left with **seven**?

5. What **five-letter word** do most American third graders **spell wrong**?

6. Is it true that **spelling** begins with an **S** and ends with an **E**?

7. **Riddle rulers really rock**. Can you spell that sentence without using the **letter R**?

All in the Family

These puzzles all have to do with **families**—mothers, fathers, sisters, brothers, and the like. See how you do!

1. Sherry and Terry are the **same age**, look ***exactly* alike**, and have **the same parents**. Yet they're **not twins**. How can you explain this?

2. **Two fathers and two sons** went to a restaurant. Each person ordered his own hamburger. The waitress brought **three burgers**, and everyone was happy. Why?

3. Is it legal for a man to marry his **widow's sister**?

4. **John's mother**, a very worldly woman, has **seven children**. The first born, a boy, is named **Europe**. The second two are twins, named **North and South America**. The next is **Australia**, followed by **Asia** and **Africa**. What is the name of the seventh child?

5. What do you call your **mother's only sister's brother-in-law**? Your uncle? Your first cousin once removed? Something else?

6. The Sparrow family is quite large. There are **six sisters**, and each sister has **two brothers**. How many children are there in total?

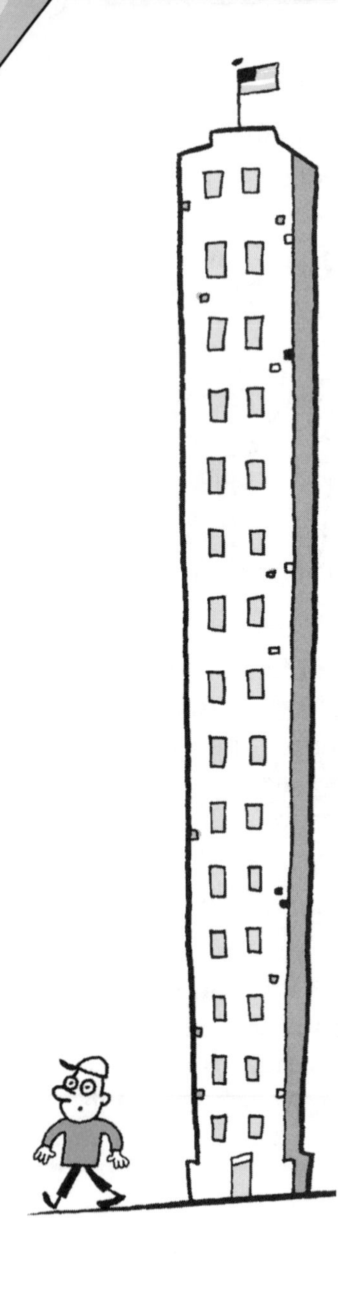

IMPOSSIBLE!

These feats seem impossible, unbelievable, preposterous, and absurd! But are they *really*? Find out for yourself!

1. A man fell out the window of a **15-story building**, but he walked away without a single broken bone or even a scrape. How'd he manage that?

2. Maria knocked **a full glass** off the edge of the kitchen counter, but no water spilled on the floor. How did that happen?

3. A basketball team won their match, but not a single man scored a basket. How did that happen?

4. You have two coins that total fifteen cents, and one of them is **not** a dim
How is this possible?

Riddle Me This

Riddles like these make ordinary things sound very strange or puzzling. Can you figure them out?

1. What business person **makes more money** the more he drives his customers away?

2. This item will **never be used** by the person who bought it and will **never be seen** by the person who *does* use it. What is it?

3. What **remains hot** no matter how long you put it in the **fridge**?

The Riddle of the Sphinx

Imagine you're walking down the street, minding your own business, when you come upon a monster that looks like a cross between a lion, a bird, and a woman. This monster introduces herself as the **Sphinx**, and she tells you that if you don't solve her riddle, she'll eat you alive! Yikes! Here's her riddle (think fast!):

What creature walks on four legs during the morning, on two legs during the middle of the day, and on three legs in the evening?

Can you think of the answer? Check page 79 to see if you got it (and prepare for the worst if you didn't—just kidding!).

The riddle of the Sphinx is a famous one from Greek mythology. In one version of the story, the Sphinx destroys a village, eating everyone who fails to correctly answer her riddle. Finally, a man named Oedipus (ED-uh-pus) solves it, and the Sphinx kills herself.

There's Something a Little...

There's something a little odd about the twelve words below. Can you figure out what it is for each one?

EXAMPLE (from page 62):

There's something a little **fishy** about this word: **fortunate**
What is it?
Answer: It has "tuna" in it.

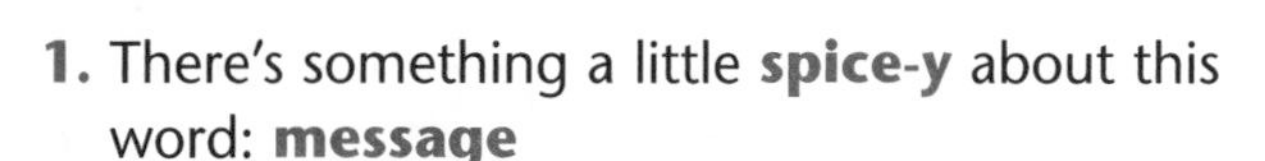

1. There's something a little **spice-y** about this word: **message**

2. There's something a little **heavy** about this word: **button**

3. There's something a little **pesky** about this word: **bugle**
4. There's something a little **wild** about this word: **cardboard**
5. There's something a little **startling** about this word: **booth**

6. There's something a little **dusty** about this word: **lattice**
7. There's something **not quite right** about this word: **leftover**
8. There's something a little **wet** about this word: **refrain**

9. There's something a little **sneaky** about this word: **hideous**
10. There's something a little **negative** about this word: **volcano**
11. There's something a little **odd** about this word: **canine**
12. There's something a little **eerie** (ear-y) about this word: **globe**

You Can Make Your Own "Something About" Riddles!

There's something a little ________________
about this word: ________________________
What is it?
Answer: ________________________

Think of an adjective to fill in the first blank (like *creepy, yucky, dark, cold,* or *mysterious*, for example), and then think of the answer to your riddle. Or, you can start with the answer and then think of the adjective. Either way, it's best if the answer is a short word (like *ton, no, bug, boo,* or *tuna*) because then you'll have an easier time with the next step.

The next step is to think of a word that your answer can **hide inside** (that goes in the second blank). The best hiding words are the ones that sound very different from the answer word, like *bug* in *bugle,* because that will throw people off the trail! It's also tougher if your hiding word has lots of letters, because then there's more to hunt through.

TEST YOUR PUZZLE POWER

Congratulations! You've reached the end of your adventures in puzzle busting, and your brainy workout is complete! How are your mental muscles feeling now? Sharper? Stronger?

Are they ready for a **final pop quiz**? That's right—here's your chance to revisit the puzzles you covered in this month's book. And it was a *lot*! If you haven't *really* covered it all yet, there's no need to rush into this quiz. If you skipped some puzzles or think you need a refresher on your strategies, go back and finish up! This quiz won't go anywhere! But if you're ready...then go for it!

1. Think of a rhyming pair that means: single star

2. Think of a word that can make a compound word with each of the following words:

black key card

3. What does this phrase box mean?

4. Can you make a square by moving two coins?

5. Which of these words will look the same when flipped upside down and reflected in a mirror?

GOOD COOKIE MADAM CHEER MICE

6. You need to measure 1 cup of water exactly. You have a 9-cup measure and a 4-cup measure. How will you do it

7. What belongs in place of the question mark?

3	1
6	2

6	3
8	4

2	3
6	9

4	2
2	?

8. Here's a coded message. If you had to guess, which letter would you say is most likely the letter E?

11-3-3-18 11-3
25-18 18-6-16-3-3
13-12 18-19-3-17

9. There's something **very hot** about this word: **unproven**. What is it?

10. From which **seven-letter word** can you take away **four letters** and be left with six?

How'd You Do?

Check your answers on page 80. Are you happy with your score? If so, GREAT! If not, it's okay. This book was filled with a bunch of challenging mind benders! Just think about it—you're probably a lot more "brainy" now than you were at the beginning of the book. And with practice, you're sure to get the next tough one that comes your way!

Answer Key

ACCESS RESTRICTED

CLEARANCE GRANTED ONLY TO THOSE WHO HAVE WRESTLED WITH PUZZLES ON PREMISES.

Page 6: POP QUIZ! What Kind of Puzzle Buster Are You?

1. *Loose* doesn't belong. Each of the other words can be spelled backward to produce another word in the list (they're "reverse anagrams" of each other). For more fun with anagrams, check out pages 14–15.

2. *Kiss* and *hiss*. You'll find more wordplay like this on pages 16–22.

3. *Top dog*. For more phrase boxes like this, turn to page 35.

4. *A toucan* (two cans). If you like this kind of word picture puzzle, check out page 34.

5. Here's one way you can draw the shape in one line:

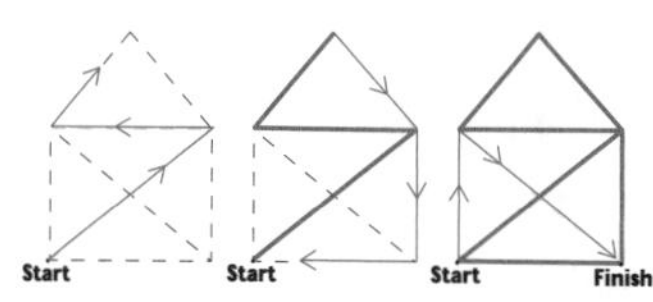

But there are other ways! To try more drawing puzzles like this (and to start learning the key to solving them), turn to page 45.

6. 5 belongs in the space with the question mark. The bottom row of each column is the sum of the top two rows (2 + 3 = 5). You'll find more puzzles like this on pages 48–49.

7. Two triangles will balance the scale. Here's how you know:

- The first scale tells you that two circles = one square.
- This means that the four circles on the second scale = two squares. So, one triangle = two squares.
- If one triangle = two squares, then you'll need *two* triangles to balance four squares!

For more puzzles like this, turn to page 52.

8. A good guess would be this symbol: ♪ That's because it's the only symbol you see standing alone, and in English, *I* is a very common one-letter word (like "A"). This is just a guess, of course! If you want to learn more code-cracking tips, turn to pages 53–56.

9. *E* is the most commonly used letter in the English language. The symbol most often used in this message is **Ø**, so this would be a good guess for *E*. Also, you might have guessed that the first word was "dear" and **Ø** is the second symbol in that word. (In case you were wondering, the message is: Dear Eve, I will meet Jeeves on Wednesday next week. I will come alone. –Ted)

10. The word "short" becomes "shorter" when you add "er"! For more riddles like this, turn to pages 61–68.

Page 11: Rhyme Time!

1. bulky kitty: fat cat
2. silly rabbit: funny bunny
3. insect embrace: bug hug
4. kind rodents: nice mice
5. unreal serpent: fake snake
6. distant sun: far star
7. female friend: gal pal
8. cranium ache: brain pain
9. no-cost plant: free tree
10. wet winner: damp champ
11. fake horse: phony pony
12. moist pooch: soggy doggy
13. large swine: big pig
14. stinky stomach: smelly belly

Page 13: Rhyme Time II: Tough Stuff!

1. stationary quaker: stuck duck
2. energetic ape: spunky monkey
3. geeky parakeet: nerdy birdie
4. self-righteous insect: smug bug
5. grumpy cat: crabby tabby
6. one-of-a-kind horse: rare mare
7. squashed bug: flat gnat
8. happy diploma-holder: glad grad

Page 14: Anagram Pairs

The starred (*) pair is a reverse anagram.

1. naked grizzly: bare bear
2. famous rodents: star rats*
3. inexpensive fuzzy fruit: cheap peach
4. feline performance: cat act
5. pale brown-colored picnic pest: tan ant
6. aching flower: sore rose
7. big syrup-producing tree: ample maple

. snake gift: serpent present

. beast teachers: monster mentors

. disliker of our planet: Earth hater

. sea-faring boat: ocean canoe

ge 16: Plus T

. ski / skit
. horns / thorns
. sew / stew
. run / runt
. win / twin
. old / told
. war / wart
. meal / metal
. boo / boot
. ouch / touch
. hear / heart
. sun / stun

ge 18: Cross Your T's!

. goal / goat
. mule / mute
. heal / heat
. bell / belt
. slop / stop
. tool / toot
. fool / foot
. slow / stow
. seal / seat

ge 19: Double Trouble!

. buy / bunny
. pale / paddle
. coin / coffin
. day / daddy
. May / marry
. gray / granny
. mule / muzzle
. mile / middle
. sale / saddle
0. Nile / nibble
1. file / fiddle

Page 21: More Double Trouble!

1. bet / beet
2. loser / looser
3. biter / bitter
4. drop / droop
5. red / reed
6. nose / noose
7. stop / stoop
8. rot / root

Page 22: Shhh! Silent E Pairs

1. hat / hate
2. cut / cute
3. on / one
4. to / toe
5. mat / mate

Page 23: Word Magic

Here's what we came up with—but as long as you changed one letter per step and got a new word, you're right!

1. RAGE to CALM
(4 steps)
RAGE
PAGE
PALE
PALM
CALM

2. COLD to WARM
(4 steps)
COLD
CORD
CARD
WARD
WARM

3. HAND to FOOT
(5 steps)
HAND
BAND
BOND
FOND
FOOD
FOOT

4. TALL to WIDE
(5 steps)
TALL
TALE
MALE
MADE
WADE
WIDE

5. HARD to SOFT
(6 steps)
HARD
CARD
CORD
CORE
SORE
SORT
SOFT

6. ROCK to GOLD
(7 steps)
ROCK
SOCK
SICK
SILK
MILK
MILD
MOLD
GOLD

7. DEAD to LIVE
(8 steps)
DEAD
DEAL
SEAL
SELL
FELL
FILL
FILE
FIVE
LIVE

8. SEED to ROSE
(9 steps)
SEED
FEED
FEET
FEAT
BEAT
BEST
PEST
POST
POSE
ROSE

9. MINI to HUGE
(12 steps)

MINI
MIND
MEND
LEND
LAND
HAND
HARD
HARE
HATE
HATS
HUTS
HUGS
HUGE

Page 26: Word Pyramids

1.

2.
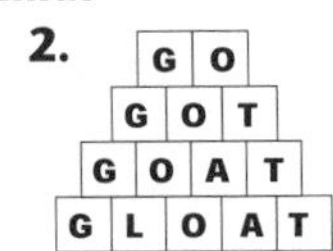

3.

4.

5.
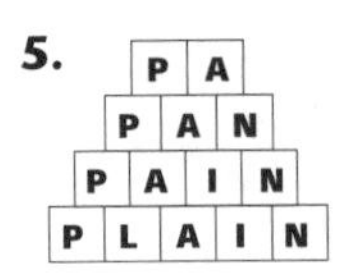

6.
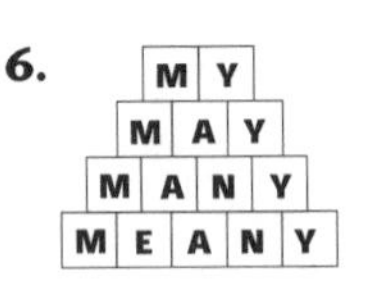

7.
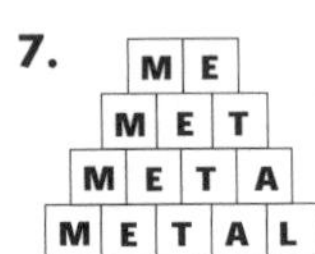

Page 29: You Can Make Your Own Pyramids!

There were lots of ways you could have filled in the pyramid, but here are two examples:

- an, man, mane, Maine
- an, ran, rain, brain

Page 29: Choco-Challenge

Here are a bunch of words that can be made out of *chocolate*:

ache, act, cat, chalet, cheat, clot, cloth, coach, coat, cola, colt, cool, cot, each, echo, etch, hale, halo, halt, hat, hate, heal, heat, hole, hot, hotel, lace, leach, let, locate, loot, oat, taco, talc, tale, teach, teal, tech, to, too, tool

Page 30: Triplets

1. chair: easy chair, armchair, wheelchair
2. man: mailman, doorman, snowman
3. boat: tugboat, lifeboat, paddle boat
4. dog: hot dog, bulldog, mad dog
5. stop: bus stop, door stop, rest stop
6. fly: butterfly, horsefly, dragonfly
7. pot: flower pot, tea pot, pothole
8. house: dog house, doll house, tree house
9. park: car park, amusement park, national park
10. ball: ball point, ball park, football
11. tree: oak tree, family tree, apple tree
12. stick: stickup, joystick, match stick
13. cheese: cheesecake, cheeseburger, blue cheese
14. machine: time machine, sewing machine machine gun
15. bird: bird brain, blue bird, bird cage
16. meal: mealtime, oatmeal, meal worm
17. pie: pie crust, mud pie, apple pie
18. car: box car, race car, carsick
19. watch: watchman, wristwatch, watch tower

Page 32: Find-a-Fruit!

To find the words, look at the numbers after each item below and look for the matching number for each letter in the grid to see the path for each word.

- **peach:** 11-7-6-5-1
- **orange:** 15-12-8-3-2-7
- **banana:** 4-8-3-6-3-6
- **plum:** 14-10-13-9
- **grape:** 16-12-8-11-7
- **apple:** 6-11-14-10-7
- **pear:** 11-7-8-12

Page 32: Dress Up!

These items can be found in the dresser:

- **tie:** 7-11-16
- **socks:** 10-5-9-13-10
- **shoe:** 10-14-15-16
- **shirt:** 10-14-11-12-7
- **shorts:** 10-14-15-12-7-3
- **vest:** 8-4-3-7
- **pants:** 2-1-6-7-3

A 1	P 2	S 3	E 4
O 5	N 6	T 7	V 8
C 9	S 10	I 11	R 12
K 13	H 14	O 15	E 16

Page 33: Desk Quest

These items can be found in the desk:

- **pencil:** 6-7-12-8-4-3
- **pen:** 6-7-12
- **paper:** 6-1-6-7-11
- **stapler:** 9-5-1-6-3-7-11
- **stamp:** 9-13-14-10-6
- **pad:** 6-1-2
- **eraser:** 7-11-14-15-16-11
- **tape:** 5-1-6-7

Page 34: A Picture's Worth ONE Word!

1. butterfly
2. blackmail
3. headline
4. mockingbird
5. password or word play

Page 34: You Can Make Your Own Picture Puzzles!

Below are *possible* answers (yours might be different):

1. bulldoze **2.** starstruck **3.** crackpot

Page 35: Phrase in a Box!

1. don't cry over spilled milk
2. fish out of water
3. two peas in a pod
4. hot under the collar
5. fingers crossed
6. wish upon a star
7. jack in the box
8. hit below the belt
9. calm before the storm
10. one in a million
11. highlight
12. read between the lines
13. cold feet
14. barking up the wrong tree
15. knock on wood
16. night falls

Page 35: You Can Make Your Own Phrase Boxes!

Here are some possible phrase boxes (these are not the only right answers!):

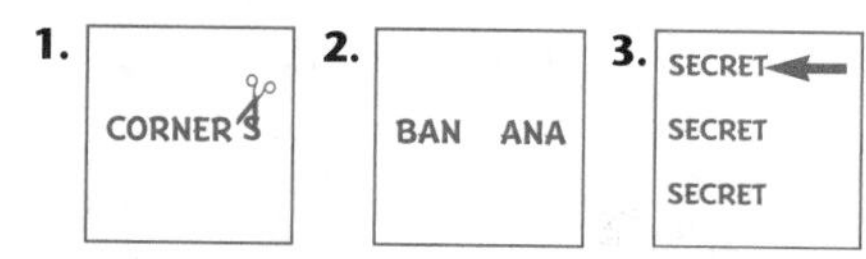

Page 40: Nice Cubes

1. A
2. D
3. **A.** The train is on the bottom
   B. The bike is on the bottom
   C. The car is on the bottom

Page 41: Nice Dice

1. **A.** 6 is on the bottom
   B. 3 is on the bottom

The secret of dice: The opposite sides always add up to seven. So one is always opposite six, two is always opposite five, and so on.

2. C is not set up properly (3 should be opposite 4).

Page 41: Mirror Mirror

1. C **2.** C **3.** B **4.** D

Bonus Question: A

Page 43: Flip Out!

1. CHICK AND OX
2. All of the words will look the same when reflected and flipped.

Page 43: Now Be a Mirror Yourself!

Page 44: Cut It Out!

1. This is how the cake can be cut:
2. This is how the pasture can be divided:

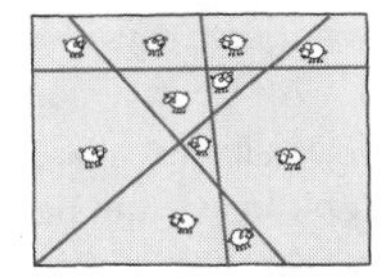

Page 45: The Drawing Room

To approach these puzzles, you have to look closely at the vertices (places where lines come together). Look for vertices that have an odd number of lines coming out of them. Those have to be your starting and ending points. If there are more than two vertices of this type in any shape, you can't draw it in one line, like #3.

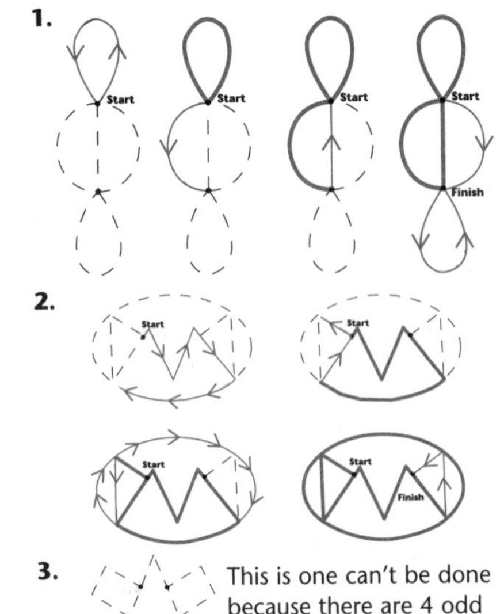

This is one can't be done because there are 4 odd number vertices.

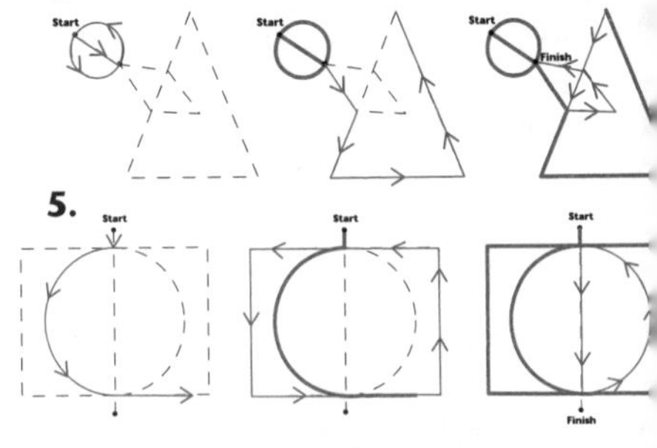

Page 46: Shifty Shapes

1. Here's how to flip the triangle upside down:

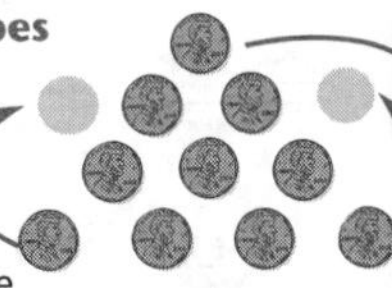

2. Here's how to make five triangles (no one said all the triangles had to be the same size!). The big outside triangle is the 5th.

Bonus Questions:

1. Here's how to turn the crab in three moves:

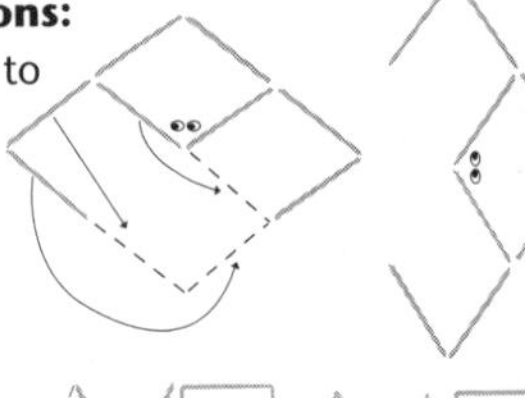

2. Here's how to turn YA into NO:

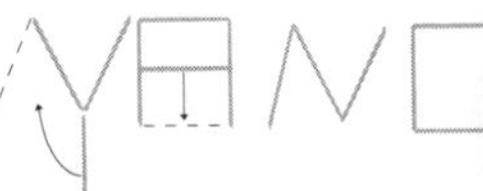

Page 48: What's Next?

1. The missing number is 10. The center number is the sum of the four numbers in the square.
2. The missing number is 1. The bottom number in the triangle is the result when you subtract the top right number from the top left number.
3. The missing number is 6. The three numbers going up are added, and the one number on the down slope is subtracted (3 + 2 + 5 - 4 = 6).
4. The missing number is 9. In this case, the numbers in the square are seen as two-digit numbers. They are subtracted to get the number in the triangle (72 - 63 = 9).
5. The missing number is 16. To get this result, the bottom numbers are added, then doubled.

Page 49: Now What's Next?

1. Every line of numbers in the star has to add up to 20. (There are 7 lines with 4 numbers in each line.) So, the missing number is 8.
2. The two numbers in each pie slice have to add up to the same total as the numbers in the opposite pie slice. So, the missing number is 1, because the total in the opposite slice is 7 (5 + 2), and 1 + 6 = 7.
3. The numbers are all multiples of 9, starting with 9 x 1 at the top left, moving to the right across the row, then down to the next row. But instead of writing 9 x 2 as 18, 1 and 8 are placed in different boxes. So, the missing number is 9 (the first digit of 90, which is 9 x 10).
4. The missing number in Pascal's Triangle is 6. Each number is obtained by adding the two numbers above it (so 3 + 3 = 6).

Bonus Question:
Here's what the next row of the triangle looks like:

1
1 1
1 2 1
1 3 3 1
1 4 6 4 1
1 5 10 10 5 1

Page 50: Mathemagic

1.

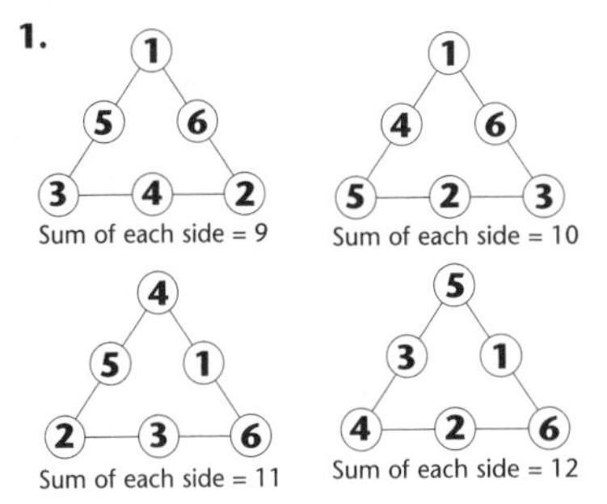

2.

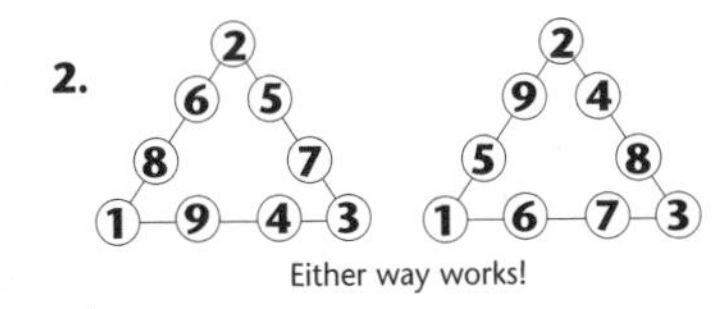

Either way works!

3.

4	9	2
3	5	7
8	1	6

Page 51: Measure Up!

1. Fill the 8-cup measure with water. Pour water from the 8-cup measure into the 3-cup measure. Pour out the 3-cup measure when it fills to the top and fill it again. After you have filled the 3-cup measure twice, you will have 2 cups remaining in the 8-cup measure.
2. Fill the 5-cup measure with sugar and dump it into the 12-cup measure. Do this again. You now have 10 cups of sugar inside the 12-cup measure. Fill the 5-cup measure one more time and pour it into the 12-cup measure. You will have 3 cups have remaining in the 5-cup measure after you have filled the 12-cup measure to the brim.
3. When you put your corn in the boiling water, turn over both timers. When the 5-minute timer runs out, turn it over again and let it run until the 6-minute timer is finished (1 minute later). Then turn the 5-minute timer over again. When it runs out after 1 minute, you will have timed 7 minutes.

Page 52: Weight a Minute!

1. You need **27 cookies.** Here's how you know:
   - The first scale tells you that 6 cookies = 3 cupcakes. That means 2 cookies = 1 cupcake.
   - If you substitute cookies for cupcakes on the left side of the second scale, you'll know that 9 cookies = 1 bread.
   - The third scale tells you that 3 breads = 1 pie. So, you now know that you'd need 27 cookies (9 x 3) to balance the pie.
2. You need **4 bananas**. Here's how you know:
   - The first scale tells you that 3 bananas + 3 apples = 3 grapefruit. That means that 1 banana + 1 apple = 1 grapefruit.
   - If you substitute 1 banana and 1 apple for the grapefruit on the left side of the second scale, you get 3 apples + 1 banana = 3 bananas. If you take a banana off of each side of this scale, you get 3 apples = 2 bananas. Phew!

- Now let's go to the final scale. Using what we know from the second scale, we can put 2 bananas and 2 apples in place of the 2 grapefruits on the left. That means we have 2 bananas and 3 apples on the left. Since we know that 3 apples = 2 bananas, we know that if we put 4 bananas on the right, the scale would balance!

Page 53: How to Be a Code Cracker

♥◘ʃ ☻◄╬↨◄♥ says TOP SECRET and
∂↨◄∞♥ ⌂◘○ says GREAT JOB.

You might have been able to guess the meanings of these words from their context (the sentences they're in).

Page 54: The Code Cracker's Sly Secrets

Here's the whole code key for the pie code. Did you spot the pattern?

The message says: **The cheese is a trap! Beware!**

Page 57: What Big Eyes You Have

The message says:

Open your eyes! There is a wolf in grandma's bed!

Again, E is the most common letter, so you can figure out that symbol. You can also guess the one-letter word, A, and the symbol after the apostrophe, S. Also, since a grandmother is mentioned in the introduction, you might guess the word "grandma." And if you know the story, you might guess "wolf," too. Here's the whole code key:

Page 58: Ode to Code

The message says:

Roses are red
Violets are blue
Codes are secret
But not from you

A	1	J	0	S	9
B	2	K	1	T	0
C	3	L	2	U	1 x
D	4	M	3	V	2 x
E	5	N	4	W	3 x
F	6	O	5	X	4 x
G	7	P	6	Y	5 x
H	8	Q	7	Z	6 x
I	9	R	8		

In this message, you could figure out E by finding the most common symbol. You cou also use the P and Q hint to guess that the letters around P and Q were underlined numbers in sequence (K = 1, L = 2, M = 3, = 4, O = 5, R = 8, and S = 9). And hopeful once you recognized "roses are red," you g "violets are blue" right away!

Page 59: Consider Yourself Warned

The messages say:

Dear Ed,
There is a bee on your head. Beware

Dear Preston,
You're stuck between a rock and a hard place.

Dear Jean,
Looks like your zipper is afraid of heights.

If you figured out (on your own or from the hint) that all the notes begin with the word dear, then you already know the symbols for D, E, A, and R. Once you know these symbols, you can recognize the sequence of the numbers, and then fill in the rest of the alphabet. Here's the code key:

A	15	J	24	S	7
B	16	K	25	T	8
C	17	L	26	U	9
D	18	M	1	V	10
E	19	N	2	W	11
F	20	O	3	X	12
G	21	P	4	Y	13
H	22	Q	5	Z	14
I	23	R	6		

Page 60: How to Make *Your* Secret Messages Safer

Look at the first letter of each item on the list. If you read vertically, the message reads "meet at two."

Page 61: Trick or Trap

1. You have five apples! Since you took the apples away, you have five.
2. The egg fell a distance of more than 15 feet. But for the first 15 feet of its fall, it remained unbroken because it was in the air!
3. Marilyn is sick of *deserts* (you know, the dry and sandy places), not *desserts*!
4. The word "fortunate" has "tuna" in it!
5. When you take two letters away from the word "alone," you're left with "one"! Same goes for any other five-letter word with "one" in it.
6. Neither—they both weigh a pound!
7. She had ten left! This question assumes you won't notice the words "all but."
8. There is no difference! 75 minutes is the same as 1 hour and 15 minutes.
9. Survivors are *never* buried—they're still alive!
10. There *is* no pony to fight over—stallions are *male* horses!

Page 64: Spelling Spree

1. sandy (the letters you could use were S *AND* Y).
2. E-G-G W-H-I-T-E (the yolk is the *yellow* part!).
3. The capital of California is spelled S-A-C-R-A-M-E-N-T-O (it's not Los Angeles).
4. seventy (take away the "ty" and you have "seven").
5. The word "wrong"!
6. Yes, "spelling" begins with an S and "ends" begins with an E.
7. Yes, you can spell T-H-A-T S-E-N-T-E-N-C-E without using the letter R!

Page 65: All in the Family

1. Sherry and Terry also have a sister named Kerry—they're *triplets*!
2. There were only three people involved: a father, a son, and a grandfather. The father is *both* a father and a son.
3. If the man has a *widow*, that means he's dead!
4. The seventh child's name is John, as it says at the beginning of the question!
5. You call him "Dad." He's your father!
6. There were eight children, six girls and two boys. (Each sister has the same two brothers.)

Page 66: Impossible!

1. He fell out of the window on the *first* floor, not the fifteenth.
2. The glass wasn't full of water—it was full of orange juice!
3. It was a *women's* basketball team.
4. One of them is *not* a dime, but the other one *is*. Your two coins are a dime and a nickel!

Page 67: Riddle Me This

1. A taxi driver
2. A coffin
3. Hot sauce (or anything hot and spicy) stays hot in the fridge!

Page 67: The Riddle of the Sphinx

A human crawls on four "legs" as a baby, walks on two legs for most of his life, and then uses a cane (the third "leg") in old age.

Page 68: There's Something a Little...

1. It has "sage" in it.
2. It has a "ton" in it.
3. It has a "bug" in it.
4. It has a "boar" in it.
5. It has "boo" in it.
6. It has an "attic" in it.
7. It has "left" in it.
8. It has "rain" in it.
9. It has "hide" in it.
10. It has "no" in it.
11. It has a "nine" in it, and nine is an odd number.
12. This is a *double* play on words. "Eerie" sounds like "ear-y," and the answer is "lobe," as in earlobe.

Page 69: Pop Quiz! Test Your Puzzle Power

1. single star = one sun
2. board: blackboard, keyboard, cardboard
3. Mess up
4. 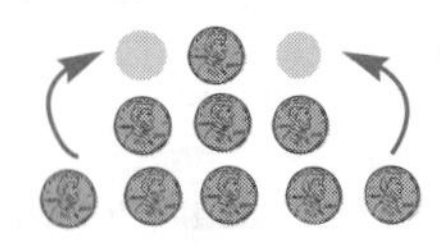
5. COOKIE
6. Fill the 9-cup measure with water and pour it into the 4-cup measure. Dump out the 4-cup measure when it's full and refill. After you've filled the 4-cup measure twice, you'll have one cup remaining in the 9-cup measure.
7. 1 belongs in place of the question mark. In each square, multiplying the numbers opposite each other diagonally results in the same number (so 2 x 2 = 4 x 1).
8. 3 is the most common number, so it would be a good guess that this number represents E.
9. It has an "oven" in it.
10. The word "sixteen" has "six" left after you remove "teen."